S0-AST-398

INSTALLING HOME AND AUTO SECURITY SYSTEMS

By
Gordon McComb

CONTRIBUTING TECHNICAL EDITOR
Harry L. Helms

THIRD EDITION

A DIVISION OF TANDY CORPORATION
FT. WORTH, TEXAS 76102

This book was developed and published by:
   Allen Publishing Group
   Richardson, Texas

Edited by:
   Ann Burns Moyer, Managing Editor
   Editorial Services, Tandy Electronics

Contributions by:
   Don French, Chief Engineer
   Consumer Products Division
   Radio Shack

Design and printing by:
   Arby Graphic Service, Inc.
   Chicago, Illinois

Acknowledgements:
   All photographs not credited are courtesy of either the author,
   Radio Shack, or the publisher.

Trademarks:
   Archer, Micronta, Mobile Alert, Plug 'n Power & Safehouse are
   registered trademarks of the Tandy Corporation.

TABLE OF CONTENTS

PREFACE

Security systems for the home and auto were once considered status symbols for the wealthy. This is not the situation today. We know you are concerned for your personal security, that of your family, home and possessions and your automobile since you have already acquired this book.

Not long ago, the U.S. Justice Department released some startling information on crime. In summary; it stated that 1 of every 133 Americans will become a murder victim, 1 of every 12 women will be the victim of rape, nearly everyone will be the victim of personal theft and 87% will be the victim of personal theft three or more times, 3 of 4 households will be burglarized at least once in 20 years, theft without forcible entry will occur in 9 of 10 homes and urban households have a 93% chance of being burglarized and rural homes 82%.

These facts are not scare tactics to entice you to install security systems. These facts remind us of the need to address our personal security requirements.

None of us can live in a castle surrounded by a moat, with a draw-bridge and maintain our personal security guards.

The author Gordon McComb and contributing technical editor Harry Helms have developed this book so that you may learn about what type of security systems could best be used to protect you and your property. That is after you have determined your security vulnerability, desired security requirements and budget for that security.

The emphasis in this book for installing security systems is for doing it yourself. You may save money while being able to customize your security system to meet your own requirements and desired protection.

May your efforts result in the degree of personal security you desire.

APG

INTRODUCTION

George Murphy closed the trunk on his late-model Olds and signaled to his family that they were ready for their big vacation. He stepped up to the front door to his house, ran through a mental checklist to make sure all the last-minute things had been done. Satisfied, he closed and locked the door. Before he turned to join his family for their drive to their favorite summer cabin, George reached in his pocket for a special key. He slid the oddly-shaped rounded key into a key switch panel beside the door, and turned it. A red light glowed, signaling all was well.

George left his house comfortable in the thought that it was being monitored—by a 24-hour guard—against fire, burglary, and vandalism. With the help of his teen-age son, George had spent the last few weekends installing a new, all-electronic alarm system. Even if the alarm never signaled a real burglary or fire, George was thankful that he took the time to install it. Instead of worrying about the disturbing increase in burglaries in his part of town, George relaxed in the thought that an electronic sentry, standing in silent vigil, looked over his house whether he was personally there to protect it or not. Yes, this would be a great vacation.

George's story is a happy one—but unfortunately, it's also not very common. Too often, homeowners trust in luck. They hope theirs will not be one of the three homes struck by burglary in a typical year, that it will happen to the other guy, and that their neighborhood is "safe."

This kind of limited thinking costs property owners billions of dollars each year due to burglary and vandalism. With increasing regularity, homeowners across the country are coming home to find theirs was the house ransacked by thieves, that it happened to them instead of the other guy, and that their neighborhood isn't as safe as they once thought it was. It is then, after the fact, that these unlucky people think about installing a security system.

Like George, you are also concerned about protecting your property while away. However, because of increased personal crimes in your city, you are equally interested in protecting yourself (if you live alone) and your family from robbery or personal attack while at your home. Keep this type of personal protection in mind when planning your security needs in chapter 1.

It doesn't need to be that way. With the simple addition of an electronic sentry—a burglar alarm system—you can greatly reduce the threat of theft and vandalism. Given the proper setup, your electronic sentry can also protect you and your family against fire or pool accidents. It can even help remind you to close the gate to keep the family dog from escaping and terrorizing the neighborhood.

Installing Home and Auto Security Systems is about making your home a safer place to live. It shows you how to design, install, and use your own alarm system. Doing it yourself not only saves you a great deal of money, it allows you to learn the ins and outs of your alarm system so that you can use it more effectively. The latest designs of security system components make the systems easier to install and less prone to false alarms. And many insurance companies allow an extra discount when your home is equipped with fire and burglary protection.

If you think that you need a degree in electronics to install an alarm system, don't worry. Even if you've never done anything electronic before in your life, you'll find there's nothing complicated about wiring your home for an alarm system. And, because modern electronic alarm systems don't use high voltages, you don't run the risk of electrocution or fire due to faulty wiring.

Many people are also installing burglar alarms in their cars. The problem with many automobile alarms is that they aren't as effective as their owners believe—unless you know how to do it right. *Installing Home and Auto Security Systems* also discusses the hows and whys of car alarm systems: how to plan for one, how to install it, and how to use it properly.

HOW TO USE THIS BOOK

The book you now hold in your hands serves many purposes. Not only is it a buyer's guide to help you select the right kind of alarm system for your home and auto, it also shows you how to install the various components. You'll learn how to wire your home so that the burglar and fire alarm sensors are as inobtrusive as possible. You'll learn the best location in the house for the control unit "brain" of the alarm system. You'll learn how to use your alarm system during the day, while you are home, to warn you that a door has been opened and that a child may be heading for danger.

While security systems are—on the whole—similar to one another, slight differences between them prevent this book from providing specific details on installing and using the exact system you own. When hooking up your alarm system, refer to the manual that accompanies it. The instruction manuals that come with the alarm system control units and components sold by Radio Shack are particularly thorough. With this book and the instructions, along with an assortment of ordinary tools, you should have no trouble installing a top-notch, professional security system.

WHAT YOU'LL FIND IN THIS BOOK

Installing Home and Auto Security Systems is divided into eight chapters. Each chapter takes a portion of the home and auto security pie and explains it in non-technical terms. Here's a short run-down of each chapter.

Chapter 1—*Home Security Basics* explains the parts of a typical alarm system, and how they work together. The chapter also explains a handy "worksheet" method of planning your own alarm system.

Chapter 2—*Security System Control Units* details the role of the control unit "brain" used at a central monitoring point. You'll learn how control units work, where to best put one in your house, and how to install it.

Chapter 3—*Security System Sensors* are the devices that actually detect a possible break-in or fire. There are many different types of security system sensors; each one is explained in this chapter.

Chapter 4—*Security System Warning Devices* tell you or someone else there may be trouble at your house. Common annunciators, detailed in this chapter, include the bell, siren, strobe lights, and telephone dialer. This chapter also explains how to test your security system and eliminate false alarms.

Chapter 5—*Self-Contained Security Devices* are a good solution to your security needs if you're unable to install a separate component system. You'll learn about the operation and use of infrared motion detectors, ultrasonic motion detectors, and self-contained door/window alarms.

Chapter 6—Automotive Security Systems discusses the various components of an automobile security system and how to select the components right for your situation. You'll also learn how to install a system in your car.

Chapter 7—Remote Paging Automotive Security Systems details exciting new auto security systems which can alert you, via a small paging receiver, when someone is tampering with your car.

Chapter 8—Case Histories presents detailed examples of typical alarm systems.

We hope you find *Installing Home and Auto Security Systems* a help in selecting and using security systems to give you peace of mind at home and for your car!

CHAPTER 1
HOME SECURITY
BASICS

Home security is more than a dead bolt on your front door. Home security is a complete network of both passive and active protection against theft, vandalism, and fire. Every piece of the system contributes to the total protection of your home. It's important that each piece of your home security system is installed properly and working the way it should.

This chapter describes how all the pieces of the home security puzzle fit together. Also included is a summary of nonelectronic security measures that you'll want to consider when planning your home protection system.

BASIC COMPONENTS

There are three parts to every security system, although they aren't always individual components:

- Control unit. This is the "brain" of the security system.
- Sensor. This detects a problem, such as smoke or a window that's been opened.
- Warning device, sometimes referred to as the alarm or annunciator. This tells you or someone else that there's a possible problem. In this book, we'll use the term *alarm* for warning devices you hear, such as bells or sirens. There are other warning devices, such as strobe lights, which "silently" indicate a possible problem.

The security system depicted in *Figure 1-1* shows examples of these three components. The control unit is housed in a protective metal box and is situated in a central location of the house (such as an indoor closet). The sensor mounts to a door or window and detects when it is opened. In a practical home security application, separate sensors would be used for each outside door and window of the house, as well as all other means of entry (cellar door, attic stairs, and so forth). The warning device is an outdoor-mounted siren that sounds in case of possible trouble. The sensor and the alarm are linked to the control unit, as shown in the block diagram in *Figure 1-2*.

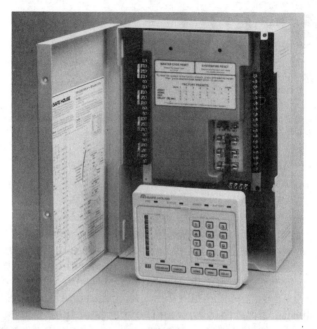

Figure 1-1: The key component of a security system is the control unit.

Separate Vs Self-Contained

The control unit and keypad *(Figure 1-1)* when used with a warning device, switches and other sensors illustrate the separate components approach to a home security system. Another approach is the self-contained security system. A typical self-contained security system is shown in *Figure 1-3*. The control unit, sensor, and alarm are contained in one easily installed cabinet. In most self-contained systems, connections on the back of the cabinet allow you to attach additional sensors and possibly an external warning device, such as an outdoor siren.

Which is better, separate component or self-contained? Both have their distinct advantages.

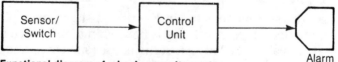

Figure 1-2: Functional diagram of a basic security system.

Advantages of Separate Component Systems

• Highly adaptable. Can be used with most any size or type of home.
• Readily expandable. Additional sensors, warning devices, and other supporting components can be installed at any time. The system grows with you.

Advantages of Self-Contained Systems

- Easily installed. Self-contained systems are designed as tabletop alarms. Position one in a room, plug it in, and it's ready to go.
- Readily moved. Because the system isn't permanently mounted, as separate component systems must be, the self-contained alarm can be moved to a different room, a better location within a room, or even a different house or apartment.

While it is impossible to say that one type of security system is better than another, as a general rule of thumb, separate component systems are used by homeowners and self-contained systems are used by home and apartment renters. Because self-contained security systems require no special installation (like mounting sensors and drilling holes) they are especially attractive to those who are on the move and don't want to invest in a piece of equipment that they must leave behind.

The greatest difference between separate component and self-contained security systems is the point of detection. The sensors used with the typical separate component alarm system are designed to detect intruders before they get inside. So that you don't falsely trigger the alarm, you must disarm it before you enter the house. An externally mounted key switch typically serves as the remote arming and disarming device.

The self-contained security system, on the other hand, is generally engineered to detect intruders after they have entered. A time delay built into the alarm allows you 15 to 30 seconds to enter the house and disable

Figure 1-3: A self-contained security system.

the alarm. If the system is not disarmed within this time period, a siren or buzzer sounds.

Some self-contained security systems also permit you to add external sensors so trouble can be detected before it has entered your house. Used in this way, the alarm sounds the instant a door or window is opened, so you must be able to disarm it yourself from the outside. Terminals on the back of the alarm cabinet allow you to attach a key switch for remote arming and disarming. In this example, the self-contained alarm functions as a hybrid control unit. It relies on its own built-in sensor as well as those you have added to it.

ASSESSING YOUR NEEDS

Several factors determine the type and complexity of your security system. You will want to weigh each of these variables before buying parts for your security system and installing them in your home. Consider carefully:

- The layout of your home
- Your ability to physically install the system components
- Your budget
- Your security requirements
- Security while away from home, while at home or both.

Layout

The layout of your home or apartment is the single most critical factor in determining the type and complexity of the security system. To fully protect against unauthorized entry, you'll need a sensor on each outside door and window that is accessible from the ground and large enough for someone to crawl through. If your home is single story, that means protecting every window and door. Windows on the second story generally need not be protected unless the window is accessible by climbing a tree or nearby retaining wall, or can't be seen from the street or by your neighbors.

Adequate fire protection requires a smoke alarm or smoke sensor in the kitchen as well as an additional smoke alarm in the common hallway off the bedrooms. If the bedrooms in your home are not situated off a common hallway, the best approach is a separate smoke alarm in each bedroom as well as in the living room, kitchen, and garage. (Chapter 5 gives detailed information about the placement of smoke alarms and sensors.)

A home or apartment with more than about four rooms (counting the living room), and many possible points of entry, does best with a separate component system. One control unit can monitor each door and window, and better control units can be connected to smoke sensors. But if your house or apartment has only two or three rooms, with few ways to enter, a self-contained security system may be all you need.

Should you want to protect an extra door or window entry, be sure to get the type of self-contained security that accepts external sensors.

The organization of your security system, as well as the number and type of sensors and warning devices you use, varies greatly depending on the design of your home or apartment. We will soon discuss a method of assessing your security needs and their solutions.

Installation

While installing a complete security system is not overly difficult, it can be time consuming and requires some forethought and attention to detail. If you are not handy with tools, and don't feel comfortable physically installing things, you may wish to opt for a self-contained security system or have someone perform the installation for you.

Some security system installations are more difficult than others. It all depends on the construction and layout of the house. A security system is harder to install in a home without an attic or basement, because the wiring can't be easily routed to different parts of the house. Alternative wiring methods can be used, such as hiding the wiring under carpets, within the floor molding or baseboards, and inside walls.

Budget

Good home security doesn't come cheap. The average cost for a self-contained system is about $80. Additional warning devices and sensors add to that cost. A complete security system using separate components, suitable for a three bedroom house, costs about $250.

There is nothing stopping you from starting your security system small, and then building upon it when your budget allows. For example, you may start with a control unit, a siren, and sensors just on the front and back doors. You can protect the windows by closing them, and locking them with window bars or stops. Then, when your budget allows, you can add additional components, such as magnet sensors for all your double-hung windows, glass-breakage detectors for the large glass patio door, smoke sensors where recommended throughout the house, and an automatic dialer so that friends, neighbors, or the proper authorities can be notified in case of a possible problem at your home.

Security Requirements

Some people feel the need for more security than others. A security system that doesn't make you feel safe is virtually useless to you. One of the greatest advantages of a home security system is peace of mind, and if you don't have that, you are not enjoying the full benefit of electronic protection.

Only you can decide how much protection you need so that you feel your home and family are secure. Still, there are ways to arrive at a more objective judgment of what is safe and what isn't. Consider the likelihood of loss by theft or fire in your neighborhood, and apply that to your security requirements checklist. Obviously, if you live in an area that's more prone to break-ins, you will feel safe only with a fairly complex security system. If you aren't sure of your neighborhood's crime record, check with your local police department and ask to see the statistics for your area. (Most police departments maintain such statistics, though not all do.)

IDENTIFY SYSTEM REQUIREMENTS

The first step in planning your system is to take a "security inventory" of each room in your home. The purpose of this is to identify doors, windows, and areas that an intruder might use to gain access to your home—in other words, you'll have to "think like a thief!"

The security inventory can be done in the form of a worksheet in which you list each room or area. Under each room, list the doors, windows, and other items an intruder might use to enter your home. Then, select appropriate switches and sensors to protect the room.

As an example, let's suppose the master bedroom of your home has one outside door leading into it, a large fixed picture window, and two smaller windows which can be opened. Your worksheet entry for the master bedroom might look like this:

Master bedroom
    Door: Plunger switch
    Picture window: Glass breakage detector
    Two smaller windows: Reed switches
    Smoke detector in hallway outside door

The example above is not the only way the master bedroom could have been inventoried. For example, you could have elected to use plunger switches on the two movable windows and a reed switch on the door, or you could have decided to simply use a passive infrared sensor for the entire bedroom. The point is that the worksheet helps you identify areas that need protection and decide how best to protect them.

At this point, you should also give some thought to the wiring of your system. How difficult will it be to run wires from the various switches and sensors back to the control unit?

UNDERSTANDING LOCAL BUILDING CODES AND REGULATIONS

When installing your security system, you don't need to make major structural changes to your home, nor do you need to install additional wiring for 120 volts ac. However, you may be required to follow local building codes and file a permit for the system with your local city or county. Because building codes and regulations differ depending on where you live, you need to contact the clerk in your county or city and ask for the details.

Generally, all that's required is that you fill out a permit for your security system and indicate whether it is for a home or business. There may be a charge for the permit. This permit may provide you some special privileges with the local police and fire departments. Make a point to check.

You are urged to comply with local regulations. Fines can be levied against those who use residential or business systems without the proper permit. In the Los Angeles area, for example, you are subject to a fine of up to $100 per day that you operate your security system without a permit. Additional fees are levied if your security system makes too many false alarms in any given time period.

One of the latest and most exciting add-ons for residential security systems is the automatic dialer, detailed more fully in Chapter 4. The dialer connects to the control unit and automatically dials up to three different phone numbers in the event of a possible fire or burglary.

Some local police departments allow the automatic dialer used in private security systems to call them in the event of a potential break-in, but not all do. Check first before you program the dialer. Some fire departments do not accept calls made by an automatic dialer. Some private security services will accept dialer calls and then make a "live" call to the police or fire department.

ADDITIONAL MEASURES

Although electronic security systems are the most fool-proof method of protecting your home and your family, you should not forget passive measures of security. These include dead bolt locks on all exterior doors, window stops, window bars, and outdoor lighting. You will also want to consider providing your home with so-called layered protection.

Security Layers

The best security systems are those composed of "layers." Layered protection simply means that if one element of your security system doesn't stop an intruder, another one will. The same applies to smoke alarms. Having several smoke alarms in your house increases the chance that at least one will be triggered in the event of a fire.

When designing your security system, think about creating layers of protection. The innermost layer is the electronic alarm protecting the entry to your home or its interior, while the outermost layer consists of passive security measures, such as lights and heavy-duty locks.

Outdoor Lighting

Although most residential burglaries occur during the daytime, a good security lighting system helps you feel safer at night and reduces the likelihood of crime in your immediate neighborhood. If your front and back porches are not already equipped with lights, that should be your first order of business. Turn them on at dusk and off at dawn. An electronic timer can automatically turn the lights on and off in case you forget.

Install supplementary floodlights if your yard is big or if readily accessible sections of your house are in shadow during the night. The lights can be controlled indoors by a switch, triggered by a timer, or automatically activated by the presence of a person. In the latter case, the floodlights are controlled by a sensitive passive infrared system.

One such infrared security floodlight system is shown in *Figure 1-4*. Upon sensing the presence of a person, the light turns on and stays on for a predetermined period of time. Passing cars and animals generally do not trigger the floodlight if it is set correctly. A built-in photoelectric cell prevents the floodlight from triggering during the daytime, thus saving energy.

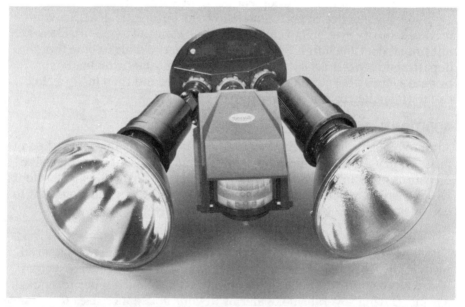

Figure 1-4: Infrared floodlight units will illuminate an area whenever they detect an intruder.

Secure Windows and Doors

Avoid thinking that just because you have a security system installed in your house, you can leave windows open and doors unprotected while you are away. It's always preferable to avoid trouble in the first place than to try to get rid of it later.

A quick look at most any police blotter will show that a number of burglaries are committed by entrance through a side or rear window. Why?

Because the windows are often partially or completely blocked from view by fences, trees, or shrubs. Inspect your windows for cracks, loose panes, and broken locks. Replace or repair as needed. The lock should be strong enough to prevent someone with average strength from being able to open the window without using tools. You can supplement the window locks by using wood or metal bars. A ½ inch diameter hardwood dowel, available at a lumber or hardware store, is a good choice for a window bar. Cut it to length and drop it in the runner between the window and the side sash.

A window stop, which consists of a piece of metal channel and a wing nut, offers more convenient protection and also allows you to open the window a few inches to let in some air. (Avoid opening the window more than about six inches, and position the stop so that it can't be tampered with from the outside.) The stop works only with aluminum windows and patio doors, however.

If your front or back door is hidden from the street or from neighbors, it may become a likely entrance point for an intruder. You can discourage a burglar from entering your house by the front or back door by making sure those doors are solid and properly hung. A security door, which typically consists of metal and a heavy wood, cannot be easily kicked in. The door is installed in its own heavy-duty metal or wood frame.

Look carefully at the locks on all your exterior doors. Add dead bolt locks to each exterior door of your house. Locks with a 1-inch or longer hardened steel shaft are the most desirable. You can purchase dead bolt locks in keyed sets so that one key will open both the front and back door. For convenience, add the dead bolt in addition to the existing door knob and lock.

Figure 1-5: Programmable timers can be used to turn on lights so you won't come home to a dark house.

Automatic Timers

Just about everyone knows that burglaries can be greatly curtailed by giving the appearance that someone is really home, when in fact the occupants may be away on a two week vacation. Automatic timers turn your lights on and off at predetermined times, making it look like someone is inside.

Timers are available in different models and configurations. The single unit programmable timer plugs between a lamp and an electrical outlet. You program it to turn on and off at specified times. The timers are available in both mechanical and electronic models, such as the one shown in *Figure 1-5.*

And there are even other ways to control interior and exterior lights and appliances. The Radio Shack Plug 'n Power *(Figure 1-6)* is a product family of wireless remote control transmitters or controllers and receivers/modules which allows you to remote control different lights or appliances while in or out of the home.

You don't like to come home to a dark driveway, porch, garage, living room or bedroom, few people do. With a Plug 'n Power transmitter and the appropriate receiver remote modules, you can turn on the selected lights from your car as you drive up to your home.

With a Remote Command Console located in your bedroom, you may turn on/off any of the lights/appliances that you have equipped with a receiver module.

The Radio Shack Plug 'n Power system uses a controller timer that allows you to set individual on and off times for up to eight modules. The modules can control lamps, appliances, and wall switches. All signals from the controller timer to the different modules are transmitted over the existing electrical wiring in your home. To prevent lights from turning off and on at the same time every day (a give-away that you aren't really home), the timer lets you select a special "security" mode that varies the on and off times each day.

The Plug 'n Power Universal Interface *(Figure 1-7)* can expand and add to the convenience, comfort and security of the basic Plug 'n Power system.

Any input to the interface that gives contact closure or low voltage (6-18V AC,DC) may be used to activate the universal interface. The input to the interface may be connected to the output from a security system and when the alarm sounds, the universal interface will send signals to the Plug 'n Power modules to flash all lights on lamp modules

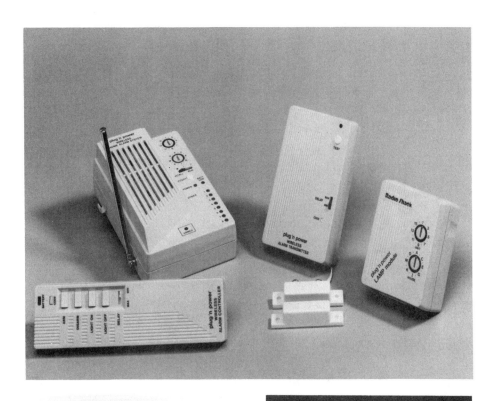

Figure 1-6: Plug 'n Power supervised security system with remote control.

Figure 1-7: Universal interface.

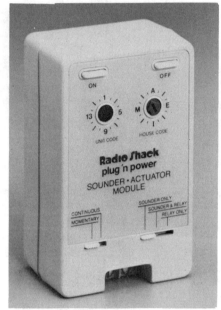

Figure 1-8: Sounder-actuator module.

and wall switch modules, and even turn on the stereo if it is connected to a module.

Uses of the universal interface are unlimited. Anything that provides contact closure or low voltage can trigger the interface. The interface thru Plug 'n Power modules could control lights, appliances or even a security alarm.

The Plug 'n Power Sounder-Actuator module *(Figure 1-8)* also will expand the Plug 'n Power system. In addition the sounder-actuator makes a beep when actuated and can be used as a relay to operate a telephone dialer, alarm or other control systems. The potential usage and applications is unlimited.

Some additional passive security measures you should consider:

- If you will be gone on a trip for less than a week or so, ask neighbor or friend to take out that week's trash for you (that is, don't leave it out several days in anticipation of pick-up day). Do the same for picking up the mail and newspaper.
- On longer trips, arrange with the post office to withhold delivery of your mail until you get back. In addition, have newspaper delivery suspended for the duration of your trip.

- Invest in an answering machine for your phone. Burglars sometimes call to see if you are home. If they get no answer, they feel it is safe to enter. A telephone answering machine will foil this tactic, if you program it with an appropriate message. *Don't* say "I'm not at home now" or something similar which indicates you're not there. A message such as "I can't get to the phone now" leaves open the possibility that you're still at home.

Keep in mind that a telephone answering machine or even some remote dialers will not work without electrical power. If your home is often without power, then the reliability of these telephone devices is reduced. Also remember, that *neither* will function if your telephone service goes out or your telephone line is rendered useless by a thief who has planned ahead.

SUMMARY
- The three basic parts of any security system are the control unit, sensors, and a warning device.
- Separate component security systems are highly adaptable and easily expandable, while self-contained systems are easily installed and readily moved.
- There is no security system that's "right" for everyone. To determine the system you need, you should first identify your security needs and requirements.
- Many cities and counties require a permit for your security system.
- Your electronic security system should be used in conjunction with passive security measures such as door and window locks and adequate lighting.

CHAPTER 2
SECURITY SYSTEM
CONTROL UNITS

The control unit is the heart of a security system. It monitors the condition of all the sensors and sounds the alarm when it detects a problem. The design of your security system will revolve around the control unit, making it very important that you choose one with care. Avoid investing in a control unit that is insufficient for the task or won't grow with you.

This chapter details the operation and installation of the typical control unit. You'll learn how control units work and where to install one in your home. This chapter covers control units only; Chapters 3 and 4 give complete details on the rest of a security system, including installing and using sensors and warning devices.

UNDERSTANDING THE TYPICAL CONTROL UNIT

While the typical control unit may look complex and unfriendly, its operation can be readily understood by studying the diagram in *Figure 2-1*. At its most basic level, the control unit is connected to switches that are either normally open (N.O.) or normally closed (N.C.). These switches

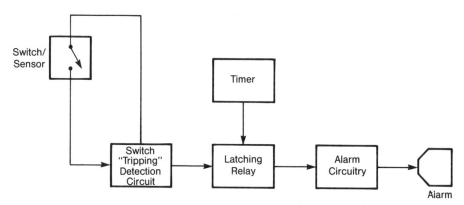

Figure 2-1: This diagram shows the internal functions of a typical control unit.

are connected in a "loop" circuit. The control detects when a switch opens or closes (depending on the type) and activates the alarm circuit in response to the operation of the switch. When the control unit has been activated by a switch, we say the security system has been "tripped." If a control unit is in operation, it (and the entire security system) is said to be "armed" or "set." If the control unit and system are not functioning, they are "disarmed."

Control units with more complex circuitry provide additional features. For example, some control units will sound the alarm for a certain period, such as five minutes, and then shut off the alarm and reset the system to detect further problems. Many control units assign priorities when signals are received from more than one loop. The loop used for fire or smoke detectors will always "override" all other loops.

A typical control unit will have instant and delayed loops. An instant loop will sound the alarm immediately when a switch is tripped, while a delayed loop will wait a specified interval. Sometimes the entire system will have a delay function. A delay circuit in the control unit can allow you time to arm the system on your way out and to disarm it when you return. If you stay inside past the predetermined time period, the alarm will sound. Most systems also allow you to install a remote key switch so that you can arm or disarm the system from outside your home.

Most control units permit turning various loops on or off as desired. This is useful when you're home and want to have certain loops on your system working, such as the smoke and fire detectors, but don't need the others.

Most control units include a mounting hole for a simple plunger-type switch, known as a tamper switch, to detect when the control unit's door has been opened. The tamper switch is on an instant loop. This prevents burglars from attempting to disable your system by damaging the control unit.

The owner's manual for your control unit will give you complete details about the various features it has.

Control Unit Switches

Switches of one type or another are the most common security system sensors, and will be used in the examples throughout this chapter. As detailed more fully in Chapter 3, alarm switches are designed so that they are normally closed or normally open. *Figure 2-2* shows the normal and tripped schematic symbols for N.O. and N.C. switches. "Loops" of such switches are connected to control units using input terminals on the control units. Some control units allow you to simultaneously connect N.O. and N.C. switch loops to the same set of terminals, as we'll discuss later.

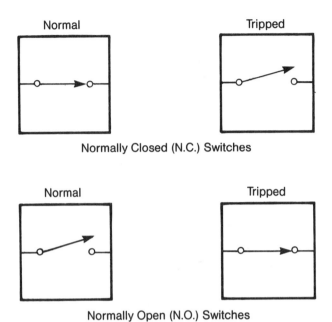

Normally Closed (N.C.) Switches

Normally Open (N.O.) Switches

Figure 2-2: Circuit symbols for normally open (N.O.) and normally closed (N.C.) switches.

Control Unit Loops

The modern control unit, as shown in *Figure 2-3*, has separate terminals for connecting to a number of switches. Each terminal identifies a different loop of switches in the system. Here's a typical setup for a four-loop security system:

- Loop 1 protects the front door.
- Loop 2 protects all the windows.
- Loop 3 protects the back door and garage.
- Loop 4 serves as a "day" alarm, discussed more fully below.

Although it may seem that all the loops serve the same purpose, there are differences between them. In the diagram in *Figure 2-4*, the control unit has four loops.

- Loop 1 has a built-in delay, and is used to let you arm and disarm the system without a remote key switch. This loop should be reserved only for those doors that you use to enter and exit the house while the security system is armed. For most homes, this is the front door only.
- Loops 2 and 3 trigger instantaneously, and are best used for protecting windows and doors not used when entering and exiting the house during system arming and disarming.

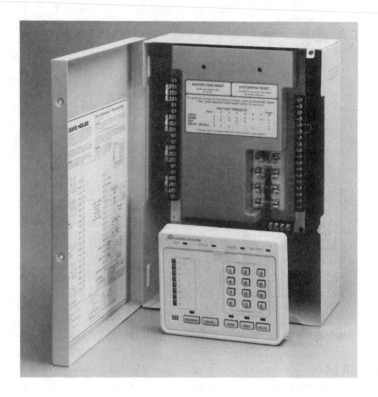

Figure 2-3: A modern control unit such as this is available at Radio Shack.

- Loop 4, the day loop, also triggers instantaneously, but is designed to activate a small buzzer instead of, or in addition to, the entire alarm. This buzzer can be used to alert you of possible danger while you are home without sounding the main alarm. You'd use the day loop, for example, to let you know if a small child has opened the gate leading to the pool or has left the house through the front or back door.

Notice that, according to the wiring diagram in *Figure 2-4*, Loops 1 and 2 can accommodate both normally open and normally closed switches, while Loops 3 and 4 accept only normally closed switches. Keep this in mind when planning your security system.

You can ignore any unused N.O. connections on the control unit. However, all unused N.C. connections must be closed using jumper wires. Otherwise, the control unit circuitry will sense an open circuit on the normally closed loop and produce an alarm.

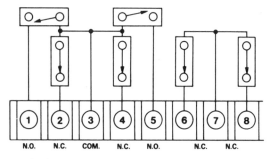

Figure 2-4: This is a typical method of connecting four different loops to a control unit.

Combining Switches on One Loop

Note that there is only one set of terminals per loop, yet you are not limited as to the number of sensors you can connect to the control unit. Each loop may consist of one or more switches wired in series or in parallel, as detailed in *Figure 2-5*. Chapter 3 provides extensive details on wiring different kinds of switches.

- To make a loop with normally closed switches, wire them in *series*. When the switch opens (signalling that a window or door is open), it breaks the N.C. actuating circuit in the control unit and the alarm sounds.
- To make a loop with normally open switches, wire them in *parallel*. When any of the switches close (an intruder has entered the house), it completes the N.O. actuating circuit in the control unit and the alarm sounds.

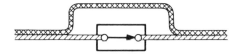

Normally Closed Device connected in series

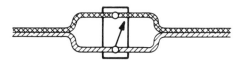

Normally Open Device connected in parallel

Figure 2-5: Methods of wiring switches in series and parallel.

A loop of N.C. switches is generally preferred over a loop of N.O. switches. This is because a N.C. loop is continuously being "checked" or supervised by the control unit. Any interruption of a N.C. loop will cause the control unit to sound the alarm. For example, the alarm will sound if the wiring connecting the switches in a N.C. loop is broken. This means potential intruders cannot defeat a N.C. loop by cutting or otherwise damaging the wiring.

Installing Wiring

The wiring connecting various sensors to the control unit should be as unobtrusive as possible, if not actually concealed.

One method is to run the wiring inside the interior walls of your home to the control unit. This method requires that you drill a small hole near the sensor. Feed one end of the wire through the hole. From the basement or attic, drill another larger hole into the sole or top plate. Feed some heavy metal "fishing" wire with a hook end into the hole. When you feel the hook end "catch" the wiring you've inserted into the wall, pull the wire from the sensor into the attic or basement.

You can also run wiring under carpeting, behind furniture, or behind floorboards and masonary trim. The wiring should be hidden as much as possible. Avoid running the wiring where it might be damaged by pets, children, or moving objects. The wiring should not be placed where it could be subjected to water or excessive moisture.

Installation Example

It's easier to visualize the use of the loops and control unit by looking at some example installations. *Figure 2-6* shows a single level house and a security system using three loops of the control unit. Loop 1 serves the front and back doors, as well as the door leading between the dining room and garage. Loop 2 protects the windows of the house. Loop 3 is not used. Loop 4 monitors when the front, back, or garage doors are opened, and is used as a day loop, while you and your family are at home. It also monitors when the gate to the pool is opened or ajar. Note that Loops 1 and 4 share the same switches. The switches for the doors and pool gate are the normally closed variety.

Loop 1 provides a delay to allow you time to manually arm and disarm the system, and most control units let you adjust the amount of time delay to suit your particular needs. By turning the delay all the way down, Loop 1 effectively triggers the instant a door is opened. By turning the delay all the way up, you give yourself up to 45 seconds to arm and disarm the system. The better control units allow you to set different exit and entry delays. For your own system, start out with an exit delay of 25 seconds and an entrance delay of 15 seconds. Adjust the times as necessary. Avoid making the entrance delay longer than absolutely necessary.

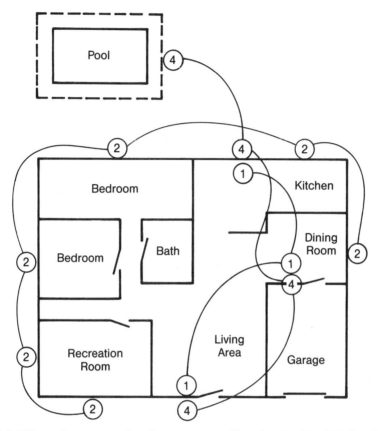

Figure 2-6: Different loops are assigned to protect specific points for this single-level home.

When the delay is turned off completely, you need some way to remotely arm and disarm the system. A key switch, shown in *Figure 2-7*, allows this. The key switch is mounted at a convenient exterior location. The key switch shown in the illustration includes a panel with two light emitting diodes (LEDs). The LEDs indicate the current state of the alarm system, and provide visual feedback that the security system is on and armed. This style of key lock is extremely difficult to "pick" and the interior of the lock panel has a tamper switch to prevent someone from defeating the alarm.

Warning Devices and Arm/Disarm Switches

The control unit is incomplete without an alarm or other warning device. Most control units connect to low voltage sirens or bells. The sirens emit a distinctive warbling high/low tone that can be heard for several city blocks. The high/low tone is most often used to indicate a possible

Figure 2-7: A key switch such as this from Radio Shack allows you to conveniently arm or disarm your security system from outside your home. Photograph by Kyle Battle.

burglary, and a steady tone or bell is used to indicate a fire. Chapter 4 discusses both types, as well as strobe lights and electronic sirens.

INSTALLATION OF THE CONTROL UNIT

You should place the control unit in some easily accessible central location in your home. This is especially true if you are not using a remote key switch to arm and disarm the unit. For example, you must be able to reach the control unit within the specified amount of time upon entering the house or the alarm will sound. More importantly, installing the control unit in an accessible area will help promote its use. A security system that isn't activated obviously can't monitor against break-ins and fire.

Picking the Right Spot

Where you place the control unit will depend on the layout of your house. Possible locations include:

- Living room closet
- Hall closet
- Bedroom closet
- Kitchen pantry

Avoid placing the control unit out in the open where an intruder might easily spot it, and never place it in an attic, basement, or garage that isn't insulated. If the control unit is subjected to extreme temperatures, it might sound false alarms or fail to function. If the room is uncomfortable to you, it is not suitable for the control unit either. Find another location for it.

Mounting the Control Unit

Most control units mount on the wall with four screws. Measure the spacing of the holes in the back of the control unit and make corresponding marks on the wall. Or, if your control unit comes with a drilling template (a piece of paper with marks for the holes), use it instead. Smooth out the template and tape it on the wall. Use a nail punch or sharp pencil to make the marks for the holes on the wall. Then, remove the paper template and drill the holes.

The type of screws you use will depend on the construction of the wall. Dryboard, gypsum, and plaster walls all require expansion or butterfly bolts. Drill a pilot hole for the bolt and hammer it into the wall. Expand the shaft by turning the head of the bolt clockwise with a long, slender-shafted screwdriver. When the shaft is fully expanded, as shown in *Figure 2-8*, retract the bolt with the screwdriver. (It will be hard to turn the screwdriver when the shaft is fully expanded.) Repeat the process for all four holes. Finally, align the holes in the control unit to the holes in the wall, insert the bolts, and tighten.

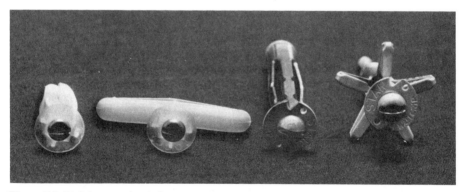

Figure 2-8: Twist expansion bolts to mount the control unit on a wall. Photograph by Kyle Battle.

If the control unit uses tear drop-shaped mounting holes, you should retract the bolts about 3/16 inch to allow for mounting space. Slide the back of the control unit over the head of each bolt. Pull down on the control unit to that the bolts sit securely in the upper part of the tear drop holes.

Other wall types require different fasteners. Always use the proper fastener or the control unit may pull out from the wall and become damaged. Use wood screws for mounting in wood, masonry screws for mounting in brick, metal screws for mounting in aluminum siding, and so forth.

Powering the Control Unit

The control unit has two forms of power: regular 120 volts ac for standard operation, and a battery backup for emergency operation. The power supply for most control units is housed in a separate transformer box, which you plug directly into any wall outlet. The transformer converts the 120 volts ac house current to 12 volts ac for the control unit. A two-conductor wire attaches the transformer to the control box.

For maximum safety and to avoid a possible fire hazard, the transformer should be plugged directly into a wall socket. Use only a wall socket that is continuously powered, not one controlled by a wall switch.

The gauge size (diameter) of the wire you need to use to power the control unit depends on the wire's length. Use the following chart as a guide. A good source of two-conductor wire is heavy-duty speaker cable, available at Radio Shack.

Length (less than)	Gauge (AWG)
20 feet	18 gauge
40 feet	16 gauge
60 feet	14 gauge

It is not recommended that you use wire lengths over 60 feet, nor that you connect the transformer to an extension cord. Although the transformer converts the house current to a safe low voltage, you should still exercise care when working with electricity. A short circuit between the two conductors coming from the transformer may cause the wire or transformer to overheat, creating a fire hazard.

Do not apply power to the control unit until you have finished wiring the sensors.

Grounding the Control Unit

Good grounding of the control unit is necessary for several reasons, including safety. To provide a good ground, attach a 14-gauge or larger insulated or uninsulated wire to any bare metal component in the control unit. A ground lug, like that in *Figure 2-9*, is usually provided inside the control unit for this purpose. Attach the other end of the ground wire securely to a cold water pipe or other good earth ground. Radio Shack sells ground rods and grounding hardware suitable for this purpose.

CAUTION: Be sure to attach the ground wire to a cold water pipe, not to a gas line. Connection to a gas line could cause a serious explosion or fire.

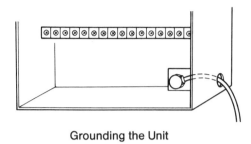

Grounding the Unit

Figure 2-9: Typical location of the lug used to ground the control unit.

INSTALLING THE REMOTE KEY SWITCH

The remote key switch allows you to arm and disarm the control unit from outside your house. If you are using a key switch, install it now on an outside wall. One good location is next to the front door, easily accessible for you when you enter and exit the house, and visible enough to serve as a deterrent to would-be intruders.

Once the key switch is installed, you can fish the wires up or down the wall and lead them to the control panel through the basement or attic. If the construction of your house doesn't permit this, see Chapter 3 for alternate ideas on how to wire your security system.

To install the key switch, trace the outline of the key switch panel on the wall. Drill several holes 1/4-inch inside the outline using a 3/16-inch bit.

NOTE: avoid drilling near the top and bottom where the mounting screws will go.

After drilling, knock out the remaining plaster or wood with a hammer and chisel. Wire the key switch as detailed in the instruction sheet that came with it. If you must use a soldering iron to attach the wires to the terminals on the key switch, use ONLY rosin core solder suitable for electronic components. DO NOT use silver solder or any solder containing an acid flux.

You will need six-conductor wire for the Radio Shack 49-535, 49-523, or 49-511 key switches. The 49-523 and 49-511 should be used with the 49-524 matching wall plate. (The wall plate provides loop and arm LEDs, as well as a convenient means to mount the key switch.) Radio Shack sells a 100 foot spool of six-conductor cable that's perfect for the job. Although one spool should suffice for most any installation, you can add more by using insulated butt connectors. Alternatively, solder the ends of the wires with a low-wattage soldering pencil and rosin core solder. Check the continuity of the wires and connectors with a meter as shown in in *Figure 2-10*.

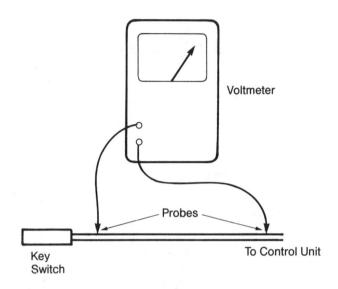

Figure 2-10: A VOM is a simple and reliable way to check the continuity of the wiring of your security system.

After wiring is complete, mount the key switch in the wall using the wood or masonry screws. Lead the wires you soldered to the key switch through the house and attach them to the control unit. For a more professional look, terminate the end of each wire with a small, solderless spade tongue. Insert the lug in the terminal on the control unit and tighten the screw.

TESTING THE CONTROL UNIT

Temporarily short all normally closed loops using a length of wire or a shorting clip supplied with the panel. Following the instructions provided with the control unit, arm (enable) each loop and turn the alarm on. If the control unit is equipped with status lights, you should see the POWER ON indicator glow. Each of the LED loop indicators should glow as well. If the panel is blank, or not working properly, double-check your work.

Checking the Loops

To determine that each loop in the alarm system works, follow these simple steps:

1. Manually disconnect the wires leading to the remote key switch terminals.
2. Disarm the system. The system should be disarmed.
3. Temporarily short the remote key switch terminals by touching a wire to them. The system should now be armed.

4. Short the terminals for one of the normally open loops. (Turn the delay time to zero if the loop is the delayed type.) The alarm should register a loop violation, usually by a green LED flashing.

Had you attached an alarm to the control unit, it would have sounded the moment the system detected the violation. To avoid bothering your neighbors with the sound of an alarm when testing your system, construct a test indicator following the schematic in *Figure 2-11*. Wire the lamp to the siren terminals on the control unit, being sure to observe correct polarity. In Chapter 4, you will learn more about sirens, lights, bells, and other alarm system warning devices, and how to install them.

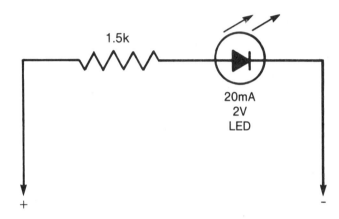

Figure 2-11: A lamp lets you check the functioning of your security system without triggering an actual alarm.

Repeat the procedure for the remaining loops. (Be sure to reset the alarm each time.) When testing a normally closed loop, temporarily remove the jumper wire or clip to activate the alarm.

Checking the Tamper Switch

Next, check the tamper switch (used in the remote key switch) by shorting its terminals on the control unit. Once again, the alarm should register a violation. The tamper switch terminals can also be used as a "panic button." A panic button is any N.O. switch connected to an instantaneously triggered loop. Panic buttons can be installed inside your house at strategic locations. If you sense danger, press the button and the alarm will sound. With most control units, you can sound the alarm with the panic button whether the system is armed or disarmed.

INSTALLING THE BACKUP BATTERIES

Backup batteries power the control unit if the electricity in your house is shut off (a typical tactic of a professional burglar). The backup batteries install conveniently in the control unit, and are kept charged until needed. The rate of discharge will depend on whether a siren or bell has been activated, but you can generally count on 1-3 hours of backup protection.

Install the batteries per the instructions provided with your control unit. The type of batteries to use will be indicated in the manual. DO NOT use non-rechargeable batteries unless the owner's manual for your control unit specifically permits their use; otherwise, serious damage to the battery and control unit could result. The Radio Shack 49-470 control unit, for example, requires the use of two 6-volt, lead-acid type rechargeable batteries. The two batteries are wired in series, as indicated in *Figure 2-12*, for a total of 12 volts.

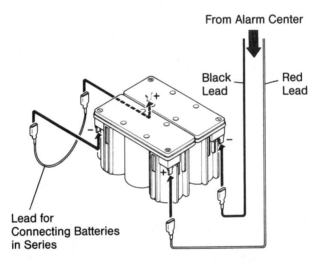

Backup Battery Connection

Figure 2-12: Adding backup batteries allows your security system to function even during power outages.

CAUTION: Use only the type of batteries specified in the control unit instruction manual.

An alarm system without backup batteries connected will always come back on armed if the ac power has been cut off.

INSTALLING ADDITIONAL ACCESSORIES

Many of the better control units can accept additional accessories. These accessories include fire and smoke sensors, telephone dialers, and pre-alarm buzzers. (The buzzer, which sounds during the delay period when entering and exiting the house while the system is armed, can also be used as a "mini-alarm" in day loops.) Follow the instructions provided with the control unit to install these devices. Fire and smoke sensors require the use of an "end-of-line" module. Be sure to properly connect the end-of-line module to the control panel. Otherwise, you may experience false alarms or the smoke sensors may not function at all.

As mentioned earlier, a plunger switch, shown in *Figure 2-13*, can be used to detect when the control unit's door is opened. If this happens, the alarm is immediately triggered. For extra protection, an additional tamper switch can be installed in the back of the control unit. This switch sounds the alarm if the control unit is removed from the wall.

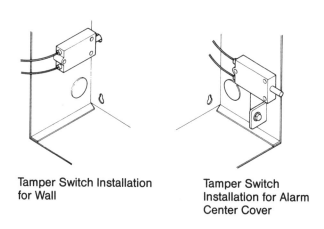

Tamper Switch Installation
for Wall

Tamper Switch
Installation for Alarm
Center Cover

Tamper Switch Installation

Figure 2-13: A plunger switch will trigger an alarm if someone tampers with the control unit.

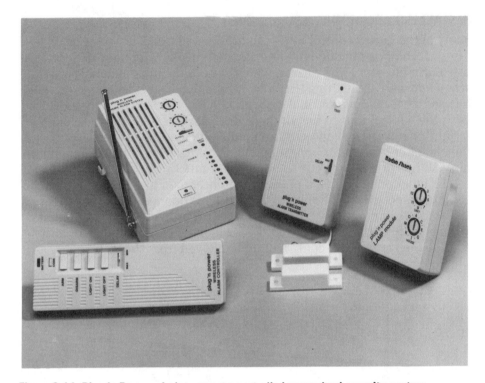

Figure 2-14: Plug 'n Power wireless remote controlled supervised security system.

WIRELESS REMOTE CONTROLLED SECURITY SYSTEM

If you have a problem with concealing the wiring to various sensors for a central control security system, this wireless system may well be the solution for you.

The Plug 'n Power wireless remote controlled supervised security system is shown in *Figure 2-14*. This system has a lot of utility. It may be used solely as a security system, or security system and Plug 'n Power light/appliance control. It may be used as part of a central control security system with the universal interface or the sounder actuator.

The wireless remote controlled security system will accept up to 16 wireless door/window transmitters. The system can also accommodate up to a total of 8 hand held transmitters.

The window/door transmitters are supervised every 90 minutes to determine battery condition and functional condition of each transmitter. The hand held transmitter can turn on lights and appliances around the house using the Plug 'n Power control modules.

SUMMARY

- Switches are connected to control units in circuit loops of normally closed (N.C.) and normally open (N.O.) types.
- N.C. loops are preferred since any interruption of such loops will trigger an alarm.
- An instant loop sounds the alarm immediately when a switch is tripped. A delayed loop will wait a specified interval before sounding an alarm.
- A remote key switch can be used to let you arm or disarm your system at a convenient point away from the control unit.
- Avoid locating the control unit where it could be easily spotted by a burglar or where it might be subjected to extreme temperatures.
- Ground the control unit to a cold water pipe or ground rod for safety.
- Check all wiring and connections in your system with a continuity meter before applying power to the control unit.
- Use an LED test indicator instead of an alarm when testing your security system.
- Install the back-up batteries specified for your control unit to power it if the electricity to your home is off.

CHAPTER 3
SECURITY SYSTEM
SENSORS

The human body has senses that relay information to the brain about the world around it. Without these senses, the human brain would be an isolated thinking machine, without connection to the outside world. The role of the sensor in security systems is similar. It relays information about the outside world to the control unit. In this capacity, the control unit is the brain, and the various sensors around your home are like the ears, eyes, nose, mouth, and skin of the human body. This chapter details the types of sensors most commonly used in residential security systems and how they work.

TYPES OF SENSORS

There are seven major types of sensors used in residential security systems alarms:

- Magnetic reed switch
- Contact switch
- Pressure mat
- Foil
- Glass breakage detector
- Photo relay
- Passive infrared sensor

Two additional sensor types, smoke and thermal, are used in residential fire systems.

All of these sensors, when designed for connection to a control unit, operate as simple switches. For example, in the application, the sensor is the switch which may be open (broken connection) during normal operation and closed during an intrusion or fire. The control unit senses when a sensor switch is closed, and sounds the alarm.

Although Chapter 2 covered operation of sensor switches, it's worth repeating here. Sensors have either one of two natural states, normally open (N.O.) or normally closed (N.C.). In security systems, the definition of "normal" is when all the doors and windows are closed, and there is no indication of an intrusion.

Magnetic Reed Switch

The magnetic reed switch, depicted in *Figure 3-1*, is the staple of modern-day security systems. The reed switch, actually composed of two separate

Figure 3-1: Magnetic reed switches such as these are good sensors for doors and windows.

pieces, works on the principle of magnetic attraction. One piece contains a large magnet, enclosed in a plastic housing. The other piece contains a set of sealed metal contacts. These contacts are positioned so that when a magnetic field is present, they are either pushed apart or pulled together, as shown in *Figure 3-2*. When the magnetic field is removed, the contacts move in the other direction.

The contacts within a N.O. reed switch do not touch when the magnetic field is near. Remove the field and the contacts close. Conversely, the contacts within a N.C. reed switch do touch when in the proximity of a magnet. Move the magnet away by opening a door or window, and the contacts open.

There are a number of styles and types of magnetic reed switches, but they all work in the same manner. The most common reed switch for

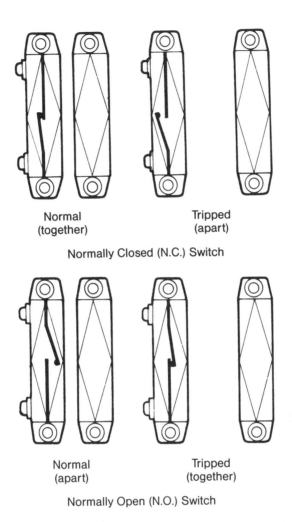

Normal
(together)

Tripped
(apart)

Normally Closed (N.C.) Switch

Normal
(apart)

Tripped
(together)

Normally Open (N.O.) Switch

Figure 3-2: "Tripped" and "untripped" positions of a magnetic reed switch.

use in residential security systems measures about 1/2 inch by 1/2 inch by 1-1/2 inches. You can purchase them in either the N.C or N.O. versions.

To install a reed switch, mount the magnet on the moving part of the door or window. The switch part mounts on the stationary door jamb or window sill, as shown in *Figure 3-3*. Plastic spacers are available at Radio Shack to adjust the height of the magnet and switch so that proper contact is made when the door or window is closed. The magnet need not be precisely aligned with the switch, but care should be exercised to avoid mounting the magnet and switch severely off axis to one another.

The construction of some windows and doors prohibit the use of conventional magnetic reed switches.

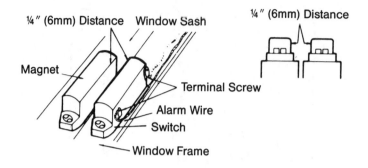

Magnet Switch Mounting on Window

Figure 3-3: Typical mounting of a reed switch.

- If space is at a premium, use mini reed switches. However, mini reed switches are more prone to the problems of misalignment and false alarms, so be careful when attaching them to your doors and windows. Get the magnet and switch as close together as possible, and make sure they are properly aligned with one another.
- A conventional reed switch triggers when the magnet is moved farther away than about an inch. A wide gap switch lets you open a window a few inches before the alarm sounds. This can be handy if the construction of the window doesn't allow close contact of the magnet and switch, or if you want to leave the window slightly open.
- Concealed magnetic switches mount inside the frame of the door or window. These require additional installation and are not recommended if you aren't handy with hand tools and working with wood. If you do use these switches, leave some slack in your wiring because they often have to be pulled out for troubleshooting.
- Windows and doors made of metals such as copper, steel, iron, and aluminum can disturb the proper operation of magnetic reed switches. One way around this problem is to use several plastic spacers to avoid mounting switches directly on the metal surface.

Contact Switch

A contact (or plunger) switch is just an ordinary spring-loaded momentary switch designed expressly for use in security applications. The plunger is oversized, and the body of the switch is designed for easy mounting to control units, doors, and windows.

When used in a control unit, the contact switch is used to prevent tampering with your security system. Switches strategically mounted on the front and back of the control unit prevent the unit from being removed or sabotaged before the alarm has a chance to do its job. You can also use plunger switches to detect when a window or door has been opened. Carefully mount the switch so that its plunger is depressed when the door or window is closed.

When used in doors, the switch can be mounted on the hinge side so that the plunger is depressed when the door is closed (see *Figure 3-4*). This type of arrangement is almost impossible for a burglar to defeat because it is not exposed from either the inside or the outside. It does, however, require careful installation.

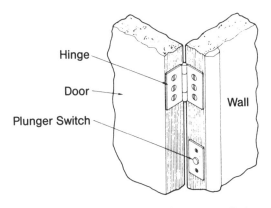

Plunger Switch Installation

Figure 3-4: The door jamb is a good location for a plunger switch.

A simple contact strip mechanism—in effect, an open switch—can be used on many windows and doors. (Its main application is in connection with window foil and vibration sensors, as detailed in the next two sections.) Like reed switches, the contact strip is composed of two parts. You mount one part on the window or door, and the other part on the frame.

One advantage of the contact strip is that you can bridge the two pieces together with a jumper cord, as shown in *Figure 3-5*, when the window or door must be left open. This application is most useful when you want to keep the security system on, but wish to temporarily defeat one or more of its sensors. This might come in handy, for example, while you are at home in the back yard. The rest of the house is still protected by the alarm, but the sliding glass door leading to the back yard is open.

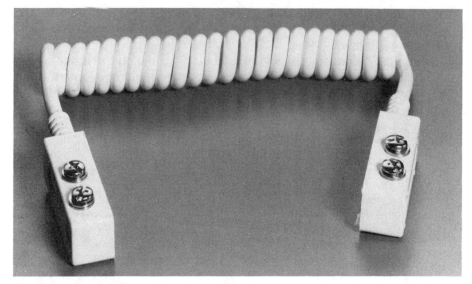

Figure 3-5: A jumper cord.

Pressure Mat

A pressure mat looks like an ordinary rubber floor mat. However, it is actually a N.O. switch. Inside the mat are two grids of switch contacts separated from each other. When the mat is stepped on, the contacts are pressed together and the N.O. switch is closed, producing an alarm. Pressure mats come in various sizes, and may be used on open floors or placed under carpets and rugs.

Foil

You've undoubtedly seen the silvery lead foil cemented around the edges of retail store windows. As you probably guessed, the foil is used to detect when a window is broken. Adhesive foil is not often used in residential burglar alarm systems, but if your home is built with many large windows you may want to consider it as an added precaution against window-entry break-ins. Foil is most often used in windows that can't be opened.

The biggest disadvantage to the foil is that you might consider it unsightly. After spending several hundred dollars for a new bay window, it seems a shame to "deface" it with burglar alarm foil. (As an alternative, you can use glass breakage detectors, discussed in the next section.) Another disadvantage is that the foil deteriorates with age. After several years, the foil can become brittle and may need to be replaced or repaired.

If you are installing the foil on a window that can be opened, you need a convenient way to disconnect the wires from the window foil block. The contact strip, available at Radio Shack and described in the previous section, is designed just for this purpose. You mount the spring section on the window itself and the contact plate on the window sill. You must mount these pieces so that the metal tabs on both sides of the switch make good contact.

The connection is made between the control unit and window foil when the window is closed. Because window foil is designed only for use with the N.C. circuits of the control unit, you cannot operate the system if the window is open. (The open contacts will signal a problem to the control unit.) When leaving the window open cannot be avoided, you can "bridge the gap" with a coiled jumper wire. The wire comes equipped with contacts that attach to the window foil block.

Glass Breakage Detector

A glass breakage detector, shown in *Figure 3-6*, detects when a window is broken or removed from the frame. The sensor is attached to the glass on the inside of your home. Although it is applied with double-sided tape, the sensor can be readily removed if required. Many glass breakage detectors can be operated either as N.C. or N.O. switches and are engineered to protect up to 32 square feet, or a window measuring about 5 by 6 feet.

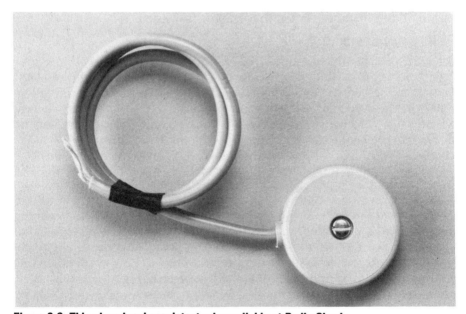

Figure 3-6: This glass breakage detector is available at Radio Shack.

There are three main types of glass breakage detectors currently available:

- Mercury switch type. Mercury is a metal that is liquid at room temperature and conducts electricity. This detector has a N.O. switch near a small "pool" of mercury. If the glass is broken or severely shaken, the mercury comes into contact with the N.O. switch terminals and closes the switch, producing an alarm.
- Weighted arm type. This uses a movable internal contact that is weighted so that it remains in one position. Vibrations or movement will make the arm move, completing or breaking an internal switch contact. This produces an alarm.
- Electronic or "tuning fork" type. This type uses an internal tuning fork which vibrates when the window is broken or jimmied. The vibrating tuning fork triggers the alarm.

All three types of glass breakage detectors are susceptible to the vibrations of a window rattling in the wind. You obtain best results when your windows are tightly installed in the frames.

You can apply a glass breakage detector along any edge of the window. To ensure that the sensor detects glass breakage for the entire pane, install it at least three inches inside the edge of the window frame. If the window is large, install separate detectors along opposite sides or corners.

As with window foil, the glass breakage detector can also use a contact strip in those instances when the window is opened.

Photo Relay Sensor

A classic method of detecting a person walking into a room is the "photoelectric eye." In modern photo relay sensors, a narrow infrared light beam is aimed across an area so that it shines directly onto a small reflector. The reflector returns the infrared beam to the photo relay sensor, where a photoelectric eye sensitive to infrared monitors it. When someone interrupts the beam, the alarm sounds. The infrared light source is not visible, so intruders cannot see and defeat this sensor. The one-piece photo relay system, as shown in *Figure 3-7*, is designed to protect an open space up to about 30 feet wide.

Passive Infrared Sensor

Let's say that an intruder has gotten past all of your home's defenses: the outdoor security lights, photo relay detector, heavy-duty dead-bolt locks, and finally the perimeter alarm connected to the windows and doors of your house. In that unlikely event, one last piece of high-tech gadgetry can detect the thief. That is the passive infrared sensor, shown in *Figure 3-8*. The sensor detects human movement and the heat given off by a person's body. And because of the way the sensor is engineered (discussed more fully below), it is largely immune to false alarms caused by thunder, loud noises, vibrations, ringing telephones, etc.

Figure 3-7: This photo relay sensor is available at Radio Shack.

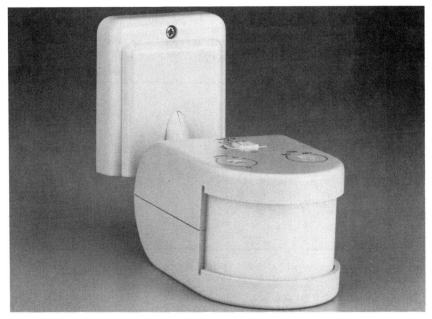

Figure 3-8: This passive infrared sensor detects changes in infrared energy levels produced by intruders.

Of course, you don't need an entire fortress of security sensors and other measures to use a passive infrared sensor. You may elect, because of your budget or other factors, to install only a passive infrared sensor in the main room of your house.

Effective use of passive infrared sensors requires a basic understanding of how they work. As shown in *Figure 3-9*, a specially made pyroelectric (heat into electricity) sensor electronically monitors the room to be protected. This sensor is sensitive to heat (infrared energy) radiated by objects. Any abrupt change in the level of infrared radiation in the room, such as that caused by the movement of an intruder, will sound the alarm. The area monitored by these sensors is divided into "zones," which are typically up to 20 feet across and 35 feet deep. Such zones are about two feet high, and movement above or below the zones is not detected. This

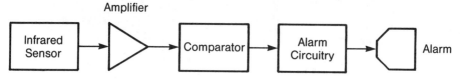

Figure 3-9: Functional block diagram of a passive infrared sensor.

helps prevent false alarms due to pets or small children. *Figure 3-10* shows top and side views of the zones monitored by the sensor shown in *Figure 3-8*. For best results, position the unit so that it is at least 5 feet above the floor. Otherwise, the lower zones may not be effective.

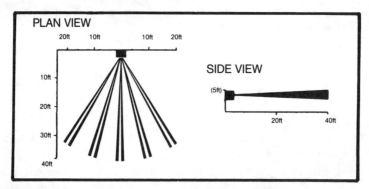

Figure 3-10: Protective coverage area of a typical infrared sensor.

Because an infrared sensor responds only to temperature changes, it generally will not produce a false alarm because of moving curtains or fan blades, air currents, etc. The sensor is best mounted high, so it points across the area to be covered. In the typical living room, for example, the sensor should be placed along a wall or in a corner so that is "sees" as much of the room as possible, including the front door, stereo rack, TV, and other items attractive to burglars. A built-in tamper switch is included with most passive infrared sensors to prevent someone from pulling the unit off the wall and defeating it before the alarm has sounded.

Smoke Sensor

An important security measure is to protect your home and family against fire. The common smoke alarm is a stand-alone unit, with its own battery power supply (or means to connect to the ac line of your house), smoke detection sensor and circuitry, and piercing alarm buzzer.

The smoke sensor, however, is designed to be connected to a control unit. (The control unit must be equipped for fire sensors.) The advantage of using a smoke sensor with a control unit is that it can activate a loud external siren or automatic telephone dialer. In the event of a fire, the siren sounds, an emergency number is dialed, or both actions are performed. With this system, someone is informed of a possible fire at your home, even when you are away. Any number of rooms can be monitored because you can install almost any number of smoke sensors in your house, wired in parallel to the control unit, as shown in *Figure 3-11*.

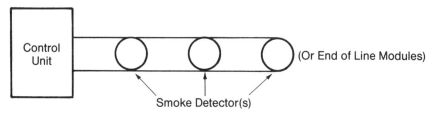

Figure 3-11: Basic parallel wiring of smoke sensors.

To be useful, the smoke sensor should be placed on the ceiling or high up on a wall. As an extra precaution, mount a separate smoke sensor in each of the bedrooms in your home or at least in the common hallway that connects to the bedrooms. See Chapter 5 for more details on the placement of smoke sensors and smoke alarms. Chapter 5 also describes the operation of smoke sensors and alarms.

Thermal Sensor

Like passive infrared sensors, thermal sensors use pyroelectric sensors. Instead of motion, however, thermal sensors sense when the temperature in a room rises above a dangerous level. The exact "trip-point" temperature varies with the design of the sensor, but is typically either 135 degrees F or 190 degrees F. You'd use the 135 degree sensor throughout your house except for the kitchen and heating furnace areas, where you would use the 190 degree sensors. This is because high temperatures are normal in the kitchen and furnace areas.

As with smoke sensors, thermal sensors are made to interface with control units specially outfitted to accept fire sensors. You can combine as many thermal sensors on one control unit loop as you wish by wiring them in parallel.

Thermal sensors are immune to false alarms produced by dust. They are especially useful in situations where fire hazards might produce more heat than smoke, such as certain types of electrical and chemical fires.

SUMMARY

- Magnetic reed switches consist of two separate pieces: a magnet in a plastic housing and a sealed metal switch. When the magnet is moved, the change in the magnetic field activates the switch.
- Plastic spacers should be used when installing magnetic reed switches on metallic surfaces.
- Contact (or plunger) switches are used to protect doors, windows, and control units.
- Metallic foil can be used to detect when a window is broken.
- Glass breakage detectors are another way to detect when a window has been broken.
- Passive infrared sensors work by detecting the heat radiated by an intruder's body.
- Smoke sensors, unlike smoke alarms, are connected directly to a control unit.
- Thermal sensors detect the heat given off by fires, and are useful in situations where fire hazards might produce more heat than smoke.

CHAPTER 4
SECURITY SYSTEM
WARNING DEVICES

Warning devices let you or someone else know there's trouble at your house. There are many types of warning devices, each one tailored to do a specific job.

- The shrill warning tone of a siren or bell can be heard for blocks, attracting attention to a would-be thief (the best measure against burglary) or warning you and others of a possible fire at your house.
- So-called "silent alarms" are telephone dialers that place an emergency call to you or someone else. A taped message indicates the suspected problem, whether fire or break-in.
- A bright strobe light serves as an extra attention getter with sound alarms. The strobe light serves as a ready beacon in a crowded neighborhood where it can be hard to pinpoint the origin of a bell or siren. A strobe light inside the home can be invaluable if one of the occupants of a house is hearing impaired.

In this chapter you'll learn about different warning devices and where to best mount them for maximum effectiveness. This chapter also details how to complete your security system by connecting one or more warning devices to the central control unit.

SIRENS AND BELLS

Security systems are most effective when they make a lot of noise. Nothing frightens away crooks better than a blaring siren and neighbors peeking out their windows to see what's going on. A siren, mounted out of the reach of the burglar, signals to you or anyone else that there's a problem and some action is necessary. Most well-designed control units automatically turn the siren off after five or ten minutes. (Laws in some communities may specify a turn-off time.)

Burglar alarms regularly use a rise-fall or European police type siren. Fire alarms use either a mechanical bell or a single-tone siren. If your control unit includes both burglar and fire circuits, be sure to use a different alarm for each one. That will help you and others easily distinguish the nature of the trouble. Radio Shack sells a number of high-power combination sirens that are capable of producing both the rise-fall tone for burglar alarms and the steady tone for fire alarms. A typical installation diagram for such siren alarms is shown in *Figure 4-1*.

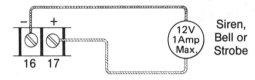

Main Alarm Connections

Figure 4-1: Main alarm connections.

When choosing a siren or bell, be sure that the control unit is rated for the power consumption of the warning device. Most sirens draw from 0.3 to 1 amp (at 12 volts dc). The main alarm terminals on your control unit should therefore be rated for at least 1 amp at 12 volts dc, or you run the risk of damaging the security system or at least blowing a fuse. The specifications sheet or instruction manual that accompanies the control unit will indicate the maximum power consumption allowed.

Note that not all sirens or bells are designed for outdoor use. Be sure to read the instructions carefully before purchasing the siren or bell. It must be weatherproof if you want to use it outdoors.

Some control units also have terminals for a "pre-alarm" buzzer. This allows you to connect a small buzzer or piezo sounder requiring 50 mA or less of current at 12 volts dc. The pre-alarm buzzer will sound during the entry delay time to remind you to disarm the system. If you're using a remote key switch, you will often not need to use a pre-alarm buzzer.

TELEPHONE DIALERS

Telephone dialers, such as the model shown in *Figure 4-2*, connect between your control unit and your regular phone line. Terminals on the control unit, typically marked "Alarm Relay Contact," connect to the appropriate connections on the dialer. (The dialer may have two separate inputs, one for fire and one for burglary. If this is the case, be sure to use the right terminals.) Power from the dialer comes either from a separate ac power adapter or from the accessory power terminals on the control unit. Most dialers also have their own built-in backup batteries. If power is removed, the dialer will still function for several hours.

Figure 4-2: Automatic message dialers.

Connection to the phone line is simple, but requires that your phone system use modular jacks, as shown in *Figure 4-3*. If your phone is "hard-wired" to the wall, or uses the old-fashioned four-prong connectors, you must upgrade your system with modular wall jacks or adapters. Radio Shack carries a full line of telephone accessories. Details on upgrading your home phone system can be found in *Installing Your Own Telephone*, available at Radio Shack.

If the phone dialer uses a magnetic tape, prerecord the message for fire and alarm trouble yourself. If the dialer uses a computerized voice, select the message you want to use.

You program the dialer with the numbers you want called in the event of a problem. Most dialers let you program up to three numbers.

As mentioned in Chapter 1, there are often some legal restrictions on using a dialer to call your local police or fire department. Be sure to contact them first to ask their permission, register your system, or obtain any necessary permit. DO NOT use the dialer without first determining the regulations in force in your community. Use only the number(s) given to you by the police and fire departments to program the dialer, and follow their instructions to the letter.

Remember that you may be subject to fines or revocation of your alarm permit if your system produces false alarms. Be sure to carefully test your system for proper operation and minimum false alarms before adding a dialer!

Figure 4-3: Modular telephone jack.

As an alternative, you can program your dialer to call neighbors, friends, or yourself if you know you'll be near a specific phone at certain times of the day. Another approach is to use a private security service. (Check the yellow pages for such businesses near you.) These companies usually employ their own armed guards who rush out to your residence and check out the alarm. You usually pay a monthly fee to retain the service and an additional charge for each call they make to your house. Be sure to read the security service company contract carefully. Know what you are getting before you sign the contract.

The telephone dialer can be installed in addition to or instead of an audible annunciator. For maximum protection, consider using both dialer and siren. The siren will frighten away a would-be burglar, and the telephone dialer will alert you or someone else you trust to check on the alarm.

STROBE LIGHT

The strobe light is a useful addition to a siren or bell alarm. The light helps your neighbors and the authorities spot your house or apartment quickly, even if they have trouble locating the source of the audible alarm. A strobe light can be useful indoors, too, especially for those with hearing problems. The strobe light connects to the control unit in parallel with the siren or bell.

If you plan to mount the strobe light outdoors (the best location for most alarm systems), be sure the light is weatherproof. Otherwise, a short circuit could result. Because the strobe light is electrically connected to the same contacts on the control unit as the siren, a short circuit could render the alarm useless.

OUTDOOR MOUNTING OF THE WARNING DEVICE

To be effective, the siren, bell, or strobe light must be mounted out of the reach of a burglar or vandal. A system is relatively worthless if a burglar can snip the wires to the siren and render the security system mute (unless, of course, you also have a telephone dialer). Therefore, be sure that the wiring is concealed or out of reach.

Mount the warning device near an eave or roof line of your house, as shown in *Figure 4-4*. If mounting hardware comes with the alarm, use it or supply your own if your installation requires it. Use masonry screws to mount the annunciator in stucco or brick walls, wood screws to mount the annunciator in wood walls. Drill a hole in the outside wall and feed the wire through to the attic. Once inside the attic, run the wires to the control unit. If your house doesn't have an attic, you'll need to find an alternate route for the wires. In all cases, strive for a completely concealed cable installation.

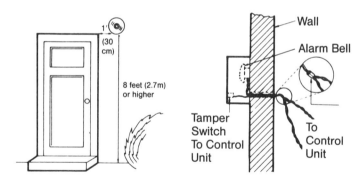

Alarm Sounder Mounted Outside

Figure 4-4: Alarm sounder mounted outside.

Avoid mounting locations where the warning device is blocked by the structure or foliage. In particular, a strobe light should be mounted so that it's visible to your neighbors or passing cars. If necessary, increase the height of the warning device by mounting it on a length of 2″ by 4″ lumber or a short metal pole (such as a television antenna mast, available at Radio Shack). If you use a metal pole, ground it for safety using the same procedure as used for an antenna mast. When using wood, tack it to the side of the house using framing nails. You can mount the metal pole using antenna mounting hardware available at Radio Shack or at a local hardware store. As an alternative, try mounting the annunciator directly on the existing mast of your TV antenna, as shown in *Figure 4-5*.

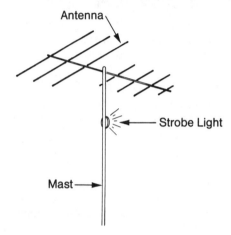

Figure 4-5: A strobe light mounted on an antenna mast.

TESTING YOUR SYSTEM

Once you have selected and installed the warning devices for your security system, you're ready to test your system for proper operation.

The first step in testing any security system is to double-check all connections before applying power to the control unit. Make sure that you haven't mixed N.O. and N.C. switches in the same loop and that you have loops connected to the proper terminals on your control unit. Because false alarms are common during initial testing, you should disconnect all warning devices. A 12 volt dc light bulb drawing 1 A or less of current can be connected to the alarm terminals instead, and will light when the system is activated. The indicator lights or LEDs on your control unit are also useful when testing your system. Consult the owner's manual for your control unit for more information.

The best approach to testing most systems is to test each loop individually by arming one loop and bypassing all others. Each switch or sensor in the unit should be checked in sequence to see if it can produce an alarm. Some items, such as glass breakage detectors or passive infrared sensors, may require some adjustment or even relocating for desired results. Try to test them under the circumstances (room temperature, etc.) that will normally be the case when the system is in operation. Some types of sensors may have built-in test circuitry. In such cases, follow the test instructions contained in the owner's manual.

Once the individual loops have been tested, check the performance of the complete system for such items as entrance/exit delay times, automatic resetting, and priority of certain loops over others. (In particular, the fire alarm loop should have priority over all others.) You should then connect all warning devices and test their operation. Be sure that anyone who might hear your alarm or receive a call from your dialer understands that it is only a test in progress!

ELIMINATING FALSE ALARMS

False alarms are more than just annoying. They undercut the effectiveness of your security system. You or others may be less inclined to pay attention to a legitimate alarm—remember the story of the little boy who cried wolf?

The first step is to determine in which loops false alarms originate. The most common cause of false alarms is sensors that are improperly installed or adjusted. For example, the sensitivity of a glass breakage detector may be set too high, and wind pressure on the glass will produce an alarm. Or, you may need to alter the spacing between a reed switch and its magnet. Make sure you have all the components of your system installed and operating as specified in the owner's manuals.

You may have to reposition sensors such as passive infrared sensors if pets and children are triggering them. Smoke sensors can also produce false alarms if located in areas where dust can accumulate inside them.

Finally, don't forget the importance of a good electrical ground for the control unit for safety. This also helps prevent stray electrical impulses from triggering the alarm.

SUMMARY

- Burglar alarms typically use a rise-fall or European police type siren, while fire alarms use a mechanical bell or single-tone siren.
- A strobe light can help locate the house or apartment an alarm is coming from. It is also useful in situations where a person has a hearing problem.
- Don't use a telephone dialer without first determining the regulations in force in your community.
- If you mount a warning device outside, make sure it is rated for outdoor use.
- The best approach to testing most security systems is to test each loop individually by arming one loop and bypassing all others.

CHAPTER 5
SELF-CONTAINED
SECURITY DEVICES

The versatility of a separate component security system is hard to excel. But, as we noted in Chapter 1, there are situations in which a self-contained system is a good choice. For example, you may be a renter who is prohibited from installing a separate component system. You might need to protect only a limited area (such as a single door or room), or you might not want to go to the trouble of drilling holes, etc., to install a separate component system. In such cases, a self-contained security system can provide valuable protection with minimal effort and cost.

While self-contained systems are simple to install and operate, this doesn't mean they're limited in their performance or capabilities. Many self-contained systems allow you to use remote key switches, alarms, telephone dialers, and similar accessories with them. Most also permit the use of battery backup power sources.

Many homeowners use self-contained security devices in conjunction with a separate component system. The self-contained systems are used to protect those areas where it is difficult or impossible to place sensors linked by wire to the control unit.

Infrared Motion Sensor System

The basic operating principles of a passive infrared motion sensor were discussed in Chapter 3. Self-contained systems built around infrared motion sensors are available, as shown in *Figure 5-1*. This unit can be thought of as an "infrared eye," because infrared energy is a form of light invisible to the eye. All warm objects radiate infrared energy. The infrared sensing element in the unit is surrounded by a reflective surface that collects infrared energy and determines the area the detector monitors. Any change in the level of infrared energy in the area "seen" by the unit is quickly sensed and sounds the internal alarm.

Like the infrared sensors discussed in Chapter 3, self-contained infrared motion sensors divide the area they protect into segments.

Figure 5-1: Self-contained infrared sensor alarms.

However, self-contained units usually have more segments and cover a wider area. The unit in *Figure 5-1* can protect an area up to 30 feet deep and 76 degrees wide. Most also include upper and lower coverage zones, as shown in *Figure 5-2*. These upper and lower zones mean that it is difficult for an intruder to "slip under" the coverage of a self-contained infrared sensor. If you have pets in your home, you can turn off the lower zones to prevent pets from triggering an alarm. The unit will be most sensitive to movement across the segments.

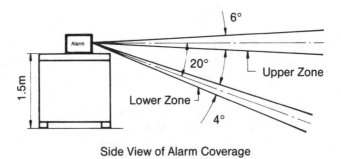

Side View of Alarm Coverage

Figure 5-2: Two different coverage zones from infrared sensor.

A self-contained infrared sensor should be placed so that its zoned area includes points, such as doors or windows, that would be logical entry points for intruders. It should also be placed so that any intruder would have to walk across its protective segments. The unit should be placed at least five feet above the floor so the lower portion of the zone will be used. Because changes in temperature cause changes in the infrared energy detected by the unit, an infrared sensor should be positioned so that direct sunlight or solar-heated walls are not in its field of view. The unit should also be aimed away from heaters, air conditioners, or other objects that might change temperature rapidly. Otherwise, false alarms may result.

The size and "shape" of the protected area of a self-contained infrared sensor is normally shown in the owner's manual and can be verified by using the unit's *test function*. In this mode, the infrared sensor is fully functional but will not sound an alarm if motion is detected. Instead, an LED on the unit will light or a soft tone will be produced. The actual coverage of the unit is found by walking through the area you want to protect, as shown in *Figure 5-3*. If there are any windows in the area you want to protect, be sure to try opening and standing in front of them. The test mode is also useful for determining if there are any sources of false alarms in the protected area.

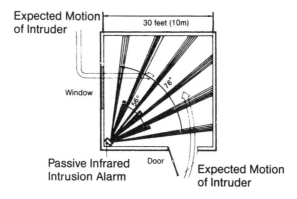

Figure 5-3: The "walk test" will determine the exact coverage of your infrared sensor.

Self-contained infrared sensors incorporate entry and exit delays, which are typically 15 or 20 seconds in length. A remote key switch can be used with most units to let you arm or disarm the system more conveniently. Terminal strip connections for an external alarm and key switch (and sometimes a backup battery) are found on the reverse of the unit. These are clearly labeled, and connections can be made as described in previous chapters.

Whenever power is first applied to an infrared motion sensor, there will be a delay of about 90 seconds before the unit becomes fully operational. This is because the unit needs time to sense the "normal" level of infrared radiation in the protected area. This is the case only when the power is switched on after being off—not when the unit is armed or disarmed.

Ultrasonic Motion Detector System

From their external appearances, ultrasonic motion detectors and infrared motion sensors seem very similar. Both incorporate motion detecting circuitry and an alarm in a single package. They're simple to install and use, and most have provision for adding external alarms and remote key switches. However, there is a major difference in the way they operate. An ultrasonic motion detector blankets the area to be protected with ultrasonic sound, at about 40 kHz in frequency, which is beyond the range of human hearing. When an intruder enters the area, echoes are produced. The detector responds to these echoes and sounds an alarm.

Instead of separate segments and zones, an ultrasonic motion detector produces a teardrop-shaped "cone" of ultrasonic energy as shown in *Figure 5-4*. This cone expands horizontally and vertically away from the unit. A typical protected area can be up to 30 feet in a forward direction and up to 20 feet wide. The actual pattern will vary with the shape and acoustical characteristics of the protected area. The pattern will not penetrate walls or glass to any great extent.

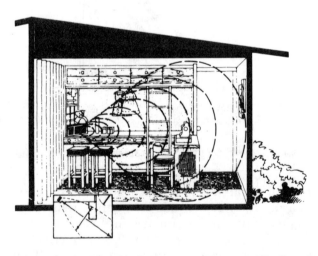

Figure 5-4: Ultrasonic motion detectors blanket an area with a protective "cone" of ultrasonic energy.

One of the best places to locate an ultrasonic motion detector is in the corner of a room you want to protect. Another good location is where the pattern will be aimed down a hallway or at an entrance that intruders are likely to use. Ultrasonic motion detectors are most sensitive to motion directly toward or away from the unit. Ultrasonic motion detectors normally include a test mode function to let you determine the coverage and performance of the unit.

Ultrasonic units use sound to detect intruders, false alarms may be produced by sources such as loud noises and ringing telephones. Moving objects such as fans or drapes near vents may also produce false alarms, as can air from heating or cooling vents. Most ultrasonic motion detectors include a control which allows you to adjust how sensitive the unit is to echoes. Careful adjustment of this control, along with proper placement of the detector, can mimimize problems with false alarms. The protected area may be tested in the same way as described for the infrared system.

RF (Microwave) Motion Detector System

The radio frequency (RF) or microwave motion detector uses high frequency radio waves, rather than ultrasonic sound, to form a protective "cone." An intruder will cause a change in the reflected radio waves sensed by the RF motion detector, causing an alarm. The performance and operation of RF motion detectors are very similar to ultrasonic units. However, RF units are more susceptible to false alarms due to RF energy radiated by electrical devices such as motors, transformers, neon signs, cable television systems, or nearby citizens band radios. For this reason, ultrasonic motion detectors are preferred over RF motion detectors.

Differences Between Infrared and Ultrasonic Detector Systems

Which is the better self-contained system, an infrared or ultrasonic type? The answer depends upon your individual needs, as each type has its own characteristics and advantages. Here's a quick summary of them:

Infrared Sensors

- Most sensitive to movement across its protected area. This makes it especially useful for protecting areas intruders must walk across when entering.
- Protects specific zones. This makes it easier to avoid possible causes for false alarms.
- Immune to false alarms caused by noise, ringing telephones, etc. Infrared units are ideal for noisy environments.

Ultrasonic Detectors

- Most sensitive to movement toward or away from it. Ultrasonic units are well suited for protecting doors, hallways, etc.
- Gives a "cone" of coverage. There are no unprotected areas within this cone.
- Immune to false alarms from temperature variations, sunlight, etc. Such units are ideal for areas where there may be sudden temperature changes.

Self-Contained Window/Door Alarms

You don't need to use a separate component security system to protect individual doors and windows. Several self-contained security devices that offer this protection are available.

Figure 5-5 shows a self-contained door/window alarm that uses a magnetic reed switch similar to those discussed in Chapter 3. The larger "box" in *Figure 5-5* houses the switch itself, an alarm, a battery, and a key switch. The smaller magnet section is installed on the moving part of the door or window, while the alarm is installed on a fixed surface so that the magnet and alarm are adjacent to each other when the door or window is closed. When the door or window is opened, the movement of the magnet triggers the loud built-in alarm.

The unit in *Figure 5-5* is armed or disarmed by a key switch, and an entrance and exit delay is provided. Both units can be mounted quickly using screws or double-sided tape. The alarm is powered by a standard 9-volt battery.

Figure 5-5: Self-contained door/window alarm.

Figure 5-6 shows a similar alarm that can also double as a door chime when it is not armed to sound the alarm. Arming and disarming the unit is done through a code entered from the keyboard. The arming/disarming code is set by the user through internal switches.

Figure 5-6: Door/window alarm and entry chime.

Smaller self-contained motion sensors are also available to protect doors and windows. *Figure 5-7* shows such a unit. It will be adequate for doors and windows, locker or mailbox covers, trailer hitches, etc. One common use for such a device is to warn when children try to gain access to a medicine cabinet. There is an entrance and exit delay of

Figure 5-7: Small self-contained motion detector.

a few seconds to allow the unit to be switched on and off without triggering the alarm. When motion is sensed, the alarm sounds for one minute and then resets. There is also a test mode so that the unit can be tested for proper coverage without producing an alarm. Power is provided by an internal 9-volt battery.

Smoke Alarms

Smoke alarms and sensors were briefly mentioned in chapter 3. Unlike smoke sensors intended for use in separate component security systems, a self-contained smoke alarm includes a built-in alarm and source of power (typically a 9-volt battery). Most smoke alarms can be installed simply by using a few screws or double-sided adhesive tape. *Figure 5-8* shows a representative smoke alarm.

There are two kinds of smoke alarms, the *ionization* and *photodiode types*. (The smoke alarm in *Figure 5-8* is the ionization type.) An ionization alarm has a small internal chamber containing a small amount of radioactive material between two electrically-charged electrodes. The air in the chamber is ionized and able to conduct an electrical current between the two electrodes. When smoke particles enter the chamber, they increase the resistance of the ionized air and thereby decrease the current flow between the electrodes. When the current flow drops below a certain point, the alarm sounds. By contrast, the photodiode alarm uses a beam of light projected across a sensing chamber onto a photoelectric cell. Smoke particles entering the sensing area reduce the light reaching

Figure 5-8: Self-contained smoke detector.

the photoelectric cell. When the light drops too low, the alarm sounds. Ionization alarms are favored in residential applications because they respond quickest to rapidly spreading fires that produce many smoke particles. Both types of alarms are able to respond to the tiny particles produced by a fire before actual smoke can be seen. This can give you and your family precious additional warning of fire danger.

When smoke particles trigger a smoke alarm, the alarm will sound until the unit is reset. The alarm in *Figure 5-8* can be reset by pushing a button on the unit. However, heavy smoke or fire will override the reset button and the unit will sound again. If there is only light smoke, the alarm may "beep" or "chirp" at intervals of approximately one minute. This warns you of lingering smoke that might be present.

It's vitally important that a self-contained smoke alarm have a fresh battery in it at all times. Some smoke alarms have a "test" button that allows you to verify proper operation of the unit. It's a good idea to check such units weekly. Other units have a LED which is on or flashes when the battery is good. Most smoke alarms will start making a loud "chirping" sound about once per minute when battery voltage drops below a certain level. The normal expected battery life can be found in the smoke alarm owner's manual. Either carbon-zinc or alkaline batteries can be used in a smoke alarm. However, alkaline batteries are preferred because they last longer, so the unit is more likely to be operational if you need it!

In addition to keeping a fresh battery in your smoke alarm, you should also keep it clean. Dust in the sensing chambers can reduce their sensitivity to actual smoke or trigger false alarms. You should clean a smoke alarm at least once a year and more often if located in a dusty or dirty environment. (For example, a smoke alarm located in the laundry room, where it might be clogged with lint, may need monthly cleaning.) You should also avoid painting a smoke alarm. Paint can get inside the unit or block the vents, affecting the smoke alarm's operation.

Placement of Smoke Alarms

The proper placement of smoke alarms (and smoke sensors) is vital if they are to give you the protection you need. This section will give you some general guidelines to follow when installing smoke alarms and smoke sensors. Many insurance companies and local fire departments have additional information, and some even offer inspections of homes and recommendations for alarm placement. You should call them before installing alarms to see what information and programs they might have available.

The basic rule in locating smoke alarms is that more *alarms mean increased protection*. There are multiple sources of fire in a home or apartment, and a single alarm will usually be unable to cover an entire dwelling satisfactorily. For maximum protection, most fire safety experts recommend a smoke alarm in *every* room of a residence. And those same experts strongly advise against relying on a single alarm for protection unless you have an exceptional situation (such as a studio apartment).

Another point to consider when locating smoke alarms is whether you can hear the alarms. If an alarm is on another floor or in another room, you may not be able to hear it.

As a minimum, smoke alarms should be located between any sleeping areas (the bedroom or several bedrooms located in the same general area) and potential fire sources such as kitchens, garages, or basements. For example, suppose you live in a single story house or apartment with two bedrooms, and these bedrooms share a common hallway. In this case, a smoke alarm should be located in the hallway outside the bedrooms. The same process should be repeated if there are two or more separate sleeping areas (such as two widely separated bedrooms). One thing to keep in mind as you decide the number of alarms you need is that smoke movement can be impeded by doors. Additional alarms should be used in fire hazard areas (such as kitchens) if there are doors between those areas and a smoke alarm.

Placement of smoke alarms is a bit more complex in dwellings with two or more stories. There should be at least one alarm on each level of the residence. Alarms should be placed near sleeping areas on all stories as described above. Smoke alarms should also be located near areas of potential fire hazards, such as heating units, hot water heaters, fuse boxes, etc.

The best location for a smoke alarm is on the ceiling at the center of the area it is intended to protect. If several alarms are installed in a hallway, they should be no more than 26 feet apart and no greater than 13 feet from the farthest wall. If it is necessary to place an alarm on a wall instead of the ceiling, the top of the alarm should be no more than a foot from the ceiling.

One special situation involves rooms with sloped, peaked, or gabled ceilings. Such ceilings have "dead air" space at their highest points, and smoke particles may not reach alarms installed at the highest points of such ceilings until too late. Fire safety experts recommend installing smoke alarms three feet from the highest points of those ceilings.

When locating smoke alarms, keep in mind those areas of your home, such as the kitchen or a fireplace, where some smoke is inevitable. Avoid installing smoke alarms in the path of normal ventilation (such as the exhaust of a kitchen range fan). You should also avoid installing smoke alarms in the path of air currents produced by fans or heating and air conditioning systems; the moving air may prevent smoke particles from entering the detector. Smoke alarms should not be installed in areas of high humidity, such as bathrooms, or in "buggy" areas where small insects might produce false alarms.

Limitations of Smoke Alarms

Smoke alarms (and sensors) do offer valuable protection for you and your family, but they do have some limitations you must keep in mind.

Fires may produce carbon monoxide, noxious fumes, and other harmful by-products. Smoke alarms do not detect such by-products and offer no protection against them. Some fires do not produce much smoke, and a smoke alarm will be less able to reliably detect them.

The proper placement of smoke alarms is essential. The previous material on locating smoke alarms should be thoroughly understood before final placement of any alarms. Remember that an alarm does little good if located in a place where it cannot be readily heard.

Smoke alarms do wear out and need replacement. Many fire safety experts recommend replacing any smoke alarm that is over ten years old. You should also replace any alarm that "chirps" or "beeps" even when a fresh battery is installed.

Total Fire Safety

Functioning smoke alarms are only one part of the total fire safety plan for your home. It makes little sense to install smoke alarms while allowing fire hazards to exist in your residence. Conditions such as oily rags, flammable liquids, exposed flames, overloaded electrical outlets, frayed wiring, etc., must be corrected to minimize the chance of a fire in the first place.

It's a good idea to have a plan of action in case of a fire. This includes escape routes from each room of your home and a place where all occupants of your home will gather in case of a fire. You and your family should all be familiar with this plan and practice the various escape routes so that they become "second nature." Needless to say, everyone in your home should be familiar with what the smoke detector alarm sounds like.

If an alarm should indeed sound in your home, your first priority should be to get out. Don't try to guess if it is a false alarm or not. In the event of a real fire, seconds can make the difference between life and death. And don't stop to gather possessions on your way out. Phone the fire department *after* you've left the building. *Never re-enter a burning building*!

In case of a fire, doors can mean either escape or danger. Touch them with your hands before opening. If they feel warm, fire may be walled up behind them. Use another escape route or stay put in such cases. If trapped inside, stay close to the floor, cover your mouth with cloth, and conserve your breath. If there is heavy smoke in a hallway or other area, cover your mouth with cloth and crawl to safety along the floor. All doors and windows should be kept closed except for escape purposes.

The surest way to survive a fire is to practice and be prepared. Be sure everyone living in your home knows what to do if a fire strikes!

SUMMARY

- Self-contained infrared motion sensors work by sensing the level of infrared (heat) energy in any area and sounding an alarm if there is any change.
- Ultrasonic motion alarms radiate ultrasonic sound and sound an alarm if echoes produced by an intruder are sensed.
- Infrared sensor alarms are best for noisy environments, while ultrasonic units are best for areas where there may be sudden temperature changes.
- Smaller self-contained security devices are available to protect a single door, window, etc.
- Ionization smoke alarms work by sensing the changes in an ionized chamber produced by smoke particles.
- Photodiode smoke alarms work by sensing the reduction in light reaching a photoelectric cell caused by smoke particles.
- Proper placement and maintenance of smoke alarms is essential for their proper operation.
- You should develop and practice a fire safety plan for your family and home.

CHAPTER 6 AUTOMOTIVE SECURITY SYSTEMS

One of the unfortunate "growth areas" for criminals in recent years has been auto theft. Once, auto theft was usually the result of kids taking a car for a "joy ride," and there was a high probability of eventually recovering the car. Things are quite different today. Car theft is often a sophisticated, organized activity in which stolen vehicles are stripped down into their individual parts at "chop shops" and then resold in "black market" transactions. Don't think that thieves would not be interested in your car just because it's not an expensive luxury model. Popular medium-priced cars are a favorite target of the new breed of auto thief because their parts can easily be sold on the black market and are in high demand.

Fortunately, the capabilities of automotive security systems have kept pace with the rise in auto theft. You can install a security system in your car that will sound an alarm if someone tries to "jimmy" open a door or the trunk. Other systems trigger an alarm if someone tries to tow or otherwise move your car. And some auto security systems include a remote pager to signal you when your car is being tampered with!

In this chapter, we'll discuss the basics of auto security systems and how to install them. In the next chapter, we'll look at systems that feature remote paging and their installation.

Components of Auto Security Systems

The basic components of an auto security system are similar to those found in home security systems:

- Control unit. As in home systems, this is the "brain." However, auto system control units tend to be much simpler than home units, with fewer loops and features.
- Sensors. Switches are the most common type of sensors. Another popular sensor is the motion detector, a type of switch designed to activate when the car is moved or shaken. Some control units incorporate a motion detector in their housing.

- Warning device. Most auto security systems are designed to sound a siren, although some blow the horn if the system is triggered. An electronic siren is preferred because of its distinctive sound and volume. *Figure 6-1* shows the elements of a basic auto security system: a control unit with a built-in motion detector, switches for the hood and trunk, and a siren.

Figure 6-1: Basic automobile security system.

There's really no such thing as a self-contained automobile security system. The layout of a car makes infrared or ultrasonic detectors impractical because they would be unable to protect vital areas such as the trunk or hood from inside the car. But the placement and installation of the components making up an auto security system are usually simpler than most home component systems.

You might be wondering if it's possible to use certain components intended for home security systems, such as magnetic reed switches, in auto security systems. The answer is no. There are major differences in the circuitry and operating environments of home and auto security systems, and the best bet is not to mix components from the two different types of systems. (However, as we'll discuss later, it's possible to use complete auto security systems to protect more than just cars.)

There's an important point you should note about auto security systems. Almost all are designed for use in cars having a 12-volt dc *negative ground* electrical system. The vast majority of cars sold in the United States and Canada use a negative ground system, but a few older or imported cars do not. If you try to install a negative ground security system in a positive ground vehicle, the electronics of the system will be destroyed. You can determine whether a vehicle has a negative or positive ground system by examining the auto battery. If the terminal marked with a minus (-) has a heavy piece of metal braid or ground cable connecting it to the metal frame, engine, or chassis, the electrical system uses a negative ground. If the positive (+) terminal is connected to the frame, the vehicle uses a positive ground system.

Passive Auto Security Measures

Like home security, auto security starts with a few common sense steps to discourage theft or vandals. These will help improve the effectiveness of your auto security system:

- Whenever possible, park in a well-lit area or where there is much car or pedestrian traffic.
- Always roll up all windows and lock all doors.
- Never leave valuables, packages, or bags where they can be seen through the windows. The best place for such items is out of sight, such as in the trunk.

Figure 6-2: Warning decals provide an extra measure of security.

- Park with your front wheels turned sharply to the right or left to discourage towing.
- Consider placing a warning decal, such as shown in *Figure 6-2*, on your car's windows or windshield. Thieves are looking for an easy time, not a hard one; most will not want to risk activating an alarm. (This is also a good step to take before you get your security system fully installed and operational!)

Switches

The most common switch used in auto security systems is the *pin switch*. You can get a good idea of how this type got its name by looking at *Figure 6-3*! The long, thin construction allows these switches to be installed in the framing around doors, the trunk, and the engine compartment. Pin switches are spring-loaded, momentary contact switches similar to the contact switches described in Chapter 3. To install them, you must drill a small hole in the desired location for the switch. The switch is then inserted and threaded in with a wrench. The switches are self-tapping and lock into place when turned. They should be turned until the pin can be depressed at least 1/4" (6.35 mm) when the door, trunk, or hood is closed. Pin switches are available in short and long pin throw lengths.

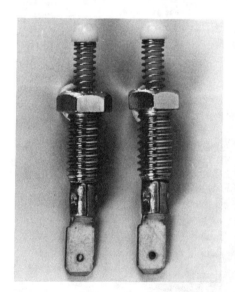

Figure 6-3: Automotive pin switches.

Pin switches have only a single wire connected to them because your car's metal chassis is used as the ground portion of the circuit. This means that pin switches must be installed only on metal surfaces.

Some auto security systems use the switches already installed in your car's door frames instead of pin switches. The switches in your car's door frames are used to turn the interior lights on when a door is opened, and are electrically identical to pin switches. Door frame switches are added to an auto security system by attaching wires from the control unit to them. This does not affect their function in turning interior lights off or on.

Some cars have delayed lighting features, which cause headlights and/or interior lights to stay on for a few seconds to a minute after entering or exiting the car. Some auto security systems (mostly those tied directly to the lighting system) are disturbed by delayed lights which confuse the self-arm or remote-arm features. If the car's light delay is longer than the exit delay of the alarm, the alarm might sound when the lights go out. Make sure that the alarm system you purchase is compatible with the lighting functions of your car.

Motion Detectors

Motion detectors are switches that are activated in response to vibration or movement. As mentioned earlier, some auto system control units (such as the one in *Figure 6-1*) include a motion detector in their housing. Separate motion detectors are also available, such as the one in *Figure 6-4*. Most motion detectors, including those in control units, have adjustable sensitivity to help minimize false alarms. Separate motion detector units are primarily designed for installation under the hood, the best location for detecting motion or vibration produced if the car is jacked, towed, or tampered with.

Figure 6-4: Electronic shock and motion sensor.

Micro Transducers

Some auto security systems use a special type of motion detector known as a *micro transducer*. These small sensors (about the size of a quarter) have small piezoelectric crystals in them. Vibration, very loud noises, or something impacting on the car will cause the piezoelectric crystals to vibrate. When they do, they produce an electric current which is sent to the control unit, producing an alarm. *Figure 6-5* shows a typical micro transducer.

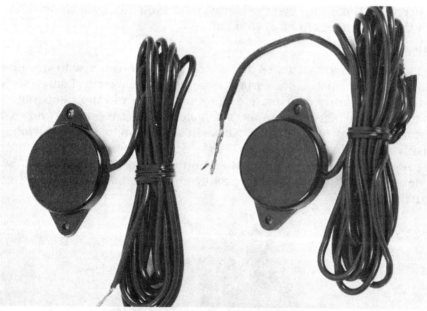

Figure 6-5: Sensitive micro transducers respond to vibration.

Keychain Remote

The keychain remote control is the new trend in auto security systems. The system shown in *Figure 6-6* has features which allow the remote to arm, disarm and even trigger the alarm up to 20 feet from the vehicle. This system also has automatic arming/disarming with entry and exit delays.

Additional features that are sometimes available with keychain remotes are valet switch, selectible security code and motion sensor on/off. The more expensive systems even have starter disable, pager and remote locator.

Figure 6-6: Auto security system with Keychain Remote.

Sirens

Sirens, such as the one in *Figure 6-7,* are the preferred method of sounding an alarm in auto security systems. Sirens come in a variety of sizes, and two types of output are popular: those that alternate rising and falling tones and those that make a "yelping" sound. Regardless of the type

Figure 6-7: Auto siren.

chosen, the siren should be installed under the hood, but away from sources of extreme heat. The siren should be pointed partially downward to avoid accumulation of moisture and dirt. It is also important to avoid major sound obstructions which could reduce the distance at which the alarm could be heard.

A couple of things must be kept in mind when selecting or installing a siren. Some localities have restrictions on the types of sirens that can be used. Your local Radio Shack store will be able to inform you of any that apply in your area. And most auto security systems require the siren to be connected to the control unit, not directly to the battery. Connecting a siren directly to the car battery will usually destroy the siren.

Control Units

As mentioned earlier, control units for auto security systems tend to be simpler than those in home systems. Fewer loops are available, and the control unit usually cannot supply power to external devices. But many auto control units have features their home counterparts don't. We've already noted that motion detectors are an integral part of numerous control units. And some control units have built-in radio transmitters that can signal a remote paging unit if the car is being tampered with. Some control units also include a radio receiver with the transmitter (forming a "transceiver" circuit), allowing the system to be armed, disarmed, or even activated by a small radio transmitter built into the pager circuit.

Entry and exit delays are a standard feature of auto control units. The length of the delay is fixed, depending upon the type of control unit, and generally can't be altered. Delays range from as little as 12 seconds to over 40 seconds. Some units have a delay only on the door or motion detector loops, while an instant loop protects the trunk and hood. Other units include a motion detector on an instant loop. Arming and disarming methods vary with control units. One simple method uses the ignition key switch to arm the unit by turning it to the ON or ACC (accessory) position for a few seconds and then switching it to OFF. The alarm then becomes active after an exit delay period. Disarming the unit is done by entering the car and switching the ignition key switch to ON before the entry delay period is up. Others are activated or disarmed by a switch on the control unit, or automatically when the ignition is switched on or off. More sophisticated control units can be armed or disarmed by using a remote transmitting unit.

Some control units produce a "beep" or other sound to indicate when the system is armed, while others use a LED. A few systems use a combination of the two.

Some newer control units have a feature known as a *valet switch*. This lets you bypass the security system in situations where you will be away from your car but the car will be attended or protected, such as valet parking, servicing, inspection, etc. The valet switch must be activated while the engine is running to bypass the security system. This prevents the valet switch circuit from being activated by intruders.

A final difference between control units is how they are mounted. Some are mounted directly to a surface, while others use a mounting bracket similar to those used for CB radios or auto stereo components.

Installing a Basic Auto Security System

The first step in installing a security system in your car is deciding where the control unit will be located. The control unit should be installed in a place that is easy for you to reach but cannot be readily spotted by intruders. Good choices include under the dashboard, under a seat, in the glove compartment, or along the fire wall. Try to avoid placing the control unit directly in the flow from a heating or cooling vent because such temperature extremes could affect the control unit's operation.

If the control unit includes a motion detector, some additional points must be considered. For proper operation of the motion detector, the control unit must be as level as possible. It should also be near the center of the car so that it will be sensitive to motion at the front and back. A location under the dash is usually a good choice.

Carefully study potential areas to install the control unit. Before making a final decision on where to locate the control unit, ask yourself the following questions:

- How easy is it to drill holes for mounting the control unit?
- Can you reach the valet and other control switches without trouble?
- Is there any wiring or a fluid line behind the spots where you will drill the mounting holes?
- Will it be difficult to run wiring for the sensors and power from the control unit to the rest of the car?

Once you have determined the control unit's location, mark locations where the mounting holes are to be drilled by holding the control unit in place (or use the drilling template if one is supplied). It is best to wait until after you have installed all sensors, made the wiring connections, and tested the system before actually mounting the control unit.

Installing Sensors

Once you have decided where to locate the control unit, you need to decide where to install the sensors. *Figure 6-8* shows a top view of a car with typical locations for various sensors indicated. The best locations for mounting various sensors on your car may be slightly different, but this diagram is a good start.

If pin switches are used, they must be positioned so that they will be depressed at least 1/4" (6.35 mm) when the hood, trunk, or door is closed.

SYSTEM AND CONNECTION LOCATIONS
1. Door micro transducer connections
2. Hood connection
3. Trunk lid connection
4. Transmitter
5. Antenna

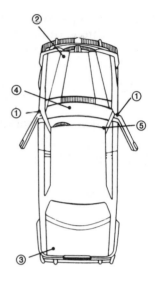

Figure 6-8: System and connection locations.

You can usually find a suitable place on the metal framing surrounding the trunk or hood compartment for mounting them. Avoid locations where the switches may not be protected from excessive contact with water. When used to protect doors, pin switches should be installed on the lower part of the door posts near the switches for the interior lights, as shown in *Figure 6-9*.

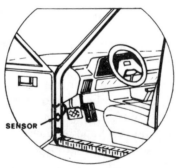

Figure 6-9: Pin switches or micro transducers locations.

Depending upon the size of the pin switch used, you will have to drill either a 1/4" (6.35 mm) or 19/64" (7.62 mm) hole in the spot you wish to install the switch. (The package the pin switch comes in will indicate the drill hole size needed.) To prevent rust and corrosion, the hole should be coated with an anti-corrosion compound or heavy grease (but nothing that would insulate the switch such as Teflon tape). Once the hole is drilled and coated, insert the pin switch and turn the switch using a wrench. A pin switch is self-tapping, and should be turned with the wrench until it locks into place.

Micro transducers are much simpler to install than pin switches because no mounting holes must be drilled. Instead, they are glued into place using an epoxy-type glue. Like pin switches, a good location for micro transducers is inside the door frame next to the switch for the interior light. Micro transducers can also be mounted on the center door posts of four-door autos as shown in *Figure 6-10*.

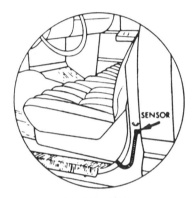

Figure 6-10: Transducer sensor on center door post.

While micro transducers are easier to install than pin switches, they can be crushed or damaged by the door if they're installed in improper locations. One good way to check if a location is suitable is through the "cookie test." Take a small cookie (such as a plain vanilla wafer) and tape it to the location you wish to install a micro transducer. Open and close the door repeatedly, and try slamming the door shut. If the vanilla wafer is not crushed, broken, or otherwise damaged, the location will be safe for the micro transducer.

Depending upon their design, separate motion detectors are either installed using a bracket or an adhesive surface on the detector. As mentioned before, a good location for a motion detector is in the engine compartment. Under the dashboard is another suitable place. The detector should be as level as possible wherever it's installed.

Using Door Frame Switches

If your security system uses the already-installed door frame light switches, you'll need to determine whether you have Ford- or General Motors-type switches in your car. The difference between these two types lies not in the switches themselves but in how they are wired. *Figure 6-11* shows circuit diagrams for both. In the Ford type, the switch is connected to +12 volts dc and the light(s) to ground; in the General Motors type, the

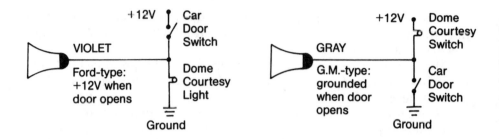

Figure 6-11: Wiring diagram for both Ford- and General Motors-type door switches.

opposite is the case. The type of switches your car uses will determine how you connect them to your system's control unit.

The names of the different types of door frame switches give a good idea of the makes of car they're used on. Here's a quick guide to their use:

- Ford type: All Ford Motor Company vehicles (Ford, Mercury, Lincoln, etc.) and a few Japanese models (mainly some Toyotas).
- General Motors type: General Motors and Chrysler vehicles and most other foreign and domestic vehicles not made by Ford, except as noted above.

If you're not sure which kind of door frame switches your car uses, you can get a good idea by visually inspecting a switch. If only one connector is going to it, that's a good (but not perfect) indication that the switch is a General Motors type. To be certain, use a voltmeter and follow these steps:

1) Open the passenger-side door and locate the door frame switch. (The switch will usually be easier to access on the passenger side.)
2) Connect the voltmeter between ground (the metal chassis) and the switch.
3) If the interior light is on, and the voltmeter reads zero volts, the switch is a General Motors type. If the voltmeter reads +12 volts, the switch is a Ford type.
4) Press and hold the switch so that the interior light goes out. If the voltmeter reads +12 volts, the switch is a General Motors type. If the voltmeter reads 0, the switch is a Ford type.

Wiring the System

To simplify connections between various components of auto security systems, a color coding scheme is used by Radio Shack and most other manufacturers of auto security products. The color code is:

- Red—this is connected to a continuous +12 V dc source to power the system. Usually the fuse block or battery is the most convenient place to make this connection.
- Black—this is the negative ground connection. Attach to a clean, bare metal contact point on the frame or fire wall of your car. It can also be connected directly to the negative (-) terminal of your car battery.
- Blue—this is the "switched" +12-volt line. Connect this to the ACC (accessory) terminal of your car's fuse block. This supplies +12 volts when the ignition is on or in the ACC position, but none when the ignition is off.
- Orange—this is another "switched" +12-volt line, but is used only to raise a retracted automatic power antenna in those systems employing a remote pager. We'll discuss this wire and its connection in the next chapter.
- Brown—this connects to the hood and trunk pin switches. Two or more switches can be connected in parallel as shown in *Figure 6-12*.
- Purple or Violet—this is connected to Ford-type door frame switches.
- Gray—this is connected to General Motors-type door frame switches.

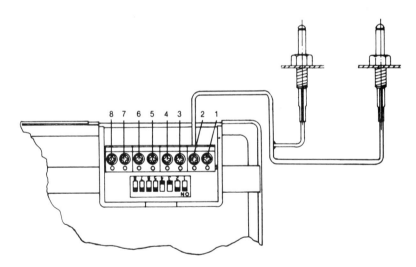

Figure 6-12: Connecting hood and trunk switches in parallel.

In addition, many systems use additional color codes for other connections necessary in those systems. For example, some systems use a white wire to identify the "hot lead" of a micro transducer. The manual for the system will identify any other color codes used. If additional wiring is needed (for pin switches, etc.), lengths of insulated 16 to 22 gauge stranded wire should be used.

When installing the wiring for your car's security system, follow these guidelines:

- Avoid sharp edges and other places that might pinch or cut the wiring.
- Run wires under carpeting in passenger areas.
- Wiring in the engine compartment should run along the fender and away from the engine and other moving parts.
- Run wiring for pin switches and the siren through the fire wall. A good place is where the speedometer cable enters the passenger compartment.
- Use tape or wiring clips to hold wiring in place.

When you make the wiring connections for your system, *always make the power (red) and ground (black) connections last.* The actual connections are simple because virtually all wiring will involve either screw terminals or "crimp" connectors. The latter are found on pin switches and most door frame switches. To make crimp connections, place an uninsulated end of the wire into the "bullet" terminal of each switch and crimp it with pliers. Then place the terminal on the end of the installed switch.

You'll have at least one unused wire from the control unit because you won't be using both the violet/purple and gray door switch wires. You'll probably have some other unused wires from your control unit (such as an orange wire if you don't have an automatic power antenna). In such cases, clip the unwanted wire(s) at or as close to the control unit as possible and insulate their ends with electrical tape.

A typical wiring diagram with color codes, for a basic auto security system is given in *Figure 6-13*. The ground connections can be made either to the metal chassis of the car or to the negative terminal of the auto battery. Don't forget that certain components, such as the siren, will also need a good connection to ground for proper operation.

Testing and Final Installation

It's a good idea to check all wiring and switches with a voltmeter or continuity checker before making the power and ground connections. If everything seems okay, switch the ignition off and connect the black wire to the auto chassis or negative terminal of the battery and the red wire to the positive (+) battery terminal. Check again with the voltmeter to see if the red wire receives +12 volts at all times. Also make sure that the switched wires (the blue and/or orange ones) don't receive power with the ignition off, but do with it on.

Once you've verified all wiring connections are correct, activate the system and try to use it according to the instructions in your owner's manual. (Some owner's manuals will include a testing procedure for the system, and that should be followed.) If your system uses micro

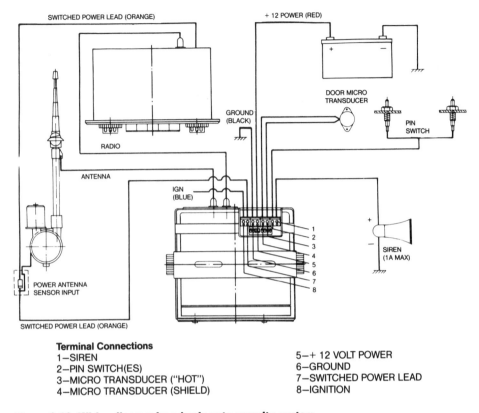

Terminal Connections

1—SIREN
2—PIN SWITCH(ES)
3—MICRO TRANSDUCER ("HOT")
4—MICRO TRANSDUCER (SHIELD)

5—+ 12 VOLT POWER
6—GROUND
7—SWITCHED POWER LEAD
8—IGNITION

Figure 6-13: Wiring diagram for a basic auto security system.

transducers or a motion detector, expect to spend some time adjusting their sensitivity to prevent false alarms.

Most problems with auto security systems are caused by failure to fully read and follow instructions or by faulty wiring. Some features, such as entry and exit delays, may appear to be serious problems if one doesn't understand how to use them. Faulty wiring can cause erratic operation or false alarms. Fortunately, most such problems are easy to trace. Check to make sure that pin switches are mounted properly and depress at least 1/4″ (6.35 mm) when the door, hood, or trunk is closed. Be sure switches, sirens, and other components have a good ground connection to the auto ground chassis. And use a voltmeter or continuity checker to see if connections are electrically sound.

SUMMARY

- The basic components of an auto security system—control unit, switches, and a warning device—are similar to those of a home security system.

- Almost all auto security systems are designed for use with 12-volt negative ground electrical systems.
- Pin switches are self-tapping and use the car's chassis as the ground portion of the circuit.
- Auto motion detectors should be mounted under the hood.
- Micro transducers are small motion detectors that can be used in place of pin switches.
- There are two types of door frame switches, the Ford- and General Motors-types. The type of switches in your car determines how they are connected to your system's control unit.
- A color coding scheme is used to identify wires connecting various components of an auto security system.
- Always make the power (red) and ground (black) connections last when wiring an auto security system.

CHAPTER 7
REMOTE PAGING
AUTOMOTIVE SECURITY
SYSTEMS

One disadvantage of the auto security systems described in the previous chapter is that someone has to hear the alarm produced by an intruder. If a car is parked in a location where no one but a thief is likely to hear the alarm, the thief may be able to disable the alarm (usually by cutting the wires to the siren) before anyone realizes something is wrong.

But there is a way to make sure that you're always aware of someone tampering with or trying to break into your car. A remote paging auto security system uses a radio transmitter installed in your car to send a warning signal to a remote paging receiver you carry with you. This transmitter is connected to the various sensors of the security system. Whenever your car is tampered with, the paging receiver will alert you so that you can investigate or call police. You can use a siren with a remote paging system, or you can just use the pager to alert you if you want to catch intruders "in the act."

Some remote paging systems have a small transmitter in the paging unit to allow them to "communicate" with your car's security system. This lets you arm or disarm the system from your pager. In addition, most pagers have a panic button function that allows you to sound your car's security system siren. This can give you welcome added security when walking to or from your car through parking lots.

How Remote Paging Systems Work

A remote paging system includes a transmitter unit (which also serves as the system's control unit) mounted in the car, and a pocket-sized remote paging receiver, as shown in *Figure 7-1*. Both the transmitter and paging receiver operate on a frequency in between the channels normally used by CB radio operators. To prevent accidental triggering of the paging receiver, a *security code* is used by the transmitter and pager. Each time the transmitter is triggered, it sends out a signal containing the security code. When the paging unit detects a signal on its frequency with the proper security code, it will start "beeping" and flashing an LED. The paging receiver ignores any signal on its frequency that does not have the proper security code. You can select your own security code for the transmitter and paging receiver and "program" it into them by setting a group of internal switches found in both units.

Figure 7-1: A basic remote paging security alarm.

The transmitter uses your car's standard radio antenna, including most that automatically raise when the radio is switched on. (However, if your car uses a wire-type antenna installed in the windshield, the effective range of the system may be significantly reduced.) If you want to extend the range of the transmitter, an ordinary CB radio antenna may be used.

The range over which the pager can receive a signal from the transmitter varies with the terrain and surrounding environment. For example, the range may be several miles in the open country but much less if your car is in an underground parking lot and you have the paging receiver with you in a high-rise office building. As a rule of thumb, you can expect a range of about two miles under most circumstances.

You can use external sensors and switches with most remote paging systems. These are installed and connected to the transmitter as described in the previous chapter. You can also install a siren if desired, and the transmitter will let you select between siren and "silent alarm" operation or use both. The transmitter operates from the car's +12-volt electrical system while the pager is powered by batteries.

Some remote pagers include an internal transmitter to allow you to send control signals back to your car's security system. This feature lets you arm or disarm the unit without worrying about entrance and exit delays. Some systems, such as the one in *Figure 7-2*, also include a panic button feature. This sounds the siren in your alarm system whenever the button is pressed. These systems also use security codes to prevent false alarms.

Figure 7-2: This advanced system includes a "panic button" feature to activate the alarm.

Installing a Remote Paging System

Except for the connections to your car's radio antenna, a remote paging security system is installed in much the same way as described in Chapter 6. However, the transmitter should be located as close to the car radio as possible to make connections to the antenna easier. *Never apply power to the transmitter unless an antenna is properly connected.* The transmitter can be badly damaged if it tries to send out signals without an antenna load connected.

If your car's antenna is a standard (non-power) type, you can connect it to the control unit/transmitter by following these steps:

1) Disconnect the antenna lead cable from the back of your car's radio.
2) Insert the antenna lead cable into the control unit-transmitter at the jack marked "ANTENNA."
3) Connect the second coaxial cable supplied with your system between the jack labeled "RADIO" on your transmitter and the antenna jack on the back of your car's radio.

If your car has a power antenna system, you need to determine if it is an automatic or semi-automatic type. An *automatic* power antenna will raise whenever the radio is turned on with the ignition switch on, while a *semi-automatic* antenna must be raised and lowered by a dash-mounted switch. *Most transmitters will not work with semi-automatic antenna systems.* If your car has a semi-automatic power antenna, the best solution is to install a CB radio antenna that can be connected to the transmitter by an adapter plug.

If your car has an automatic power antenna, you will need to use the orange switched +12-volt wire mentioned in Chapter 6 during installation of the transmitter. The orange wire will cause the antenna to be raised whenever the transmitter is about to send out an alarm signal to the remote pager. To connect your system to an automatic power antenna, follow these steps:

1) Connect the transmitter and the antenna as described for standard antennas.
2) Locate the automatic antenna's sensor input wire. This wire will usually be orange and have a male "quick disconnect" plug on it.
3) If the sensor input wire is already connected to the car radio's switched power lead, disconnect it.
4) Insert the sensor input wire's male "quick connect" plug into the orange transmitter wire's female "quick connect" plug.
5) Insert the orange wire's male plug into the female plug of the radio's switched power lead.
6) Connect the other end of the orange wire to the appropriate labeled terminal of the control unit/transmitter.

CAUTION: Failure to carefully follow the above steps may cause damage to your car's radio whenever the transmitter sends an alarm signal.

Figure 7-3 shows the connections described above. After you've finished connecting the transmitter to the antenna, you may have to adjust the antenna trimmer of your car radio for best AM reception.

Selecting Security Codes

Before testing your remote paging system, you must program the same security codes into the transmitter and remote pager. This is done by

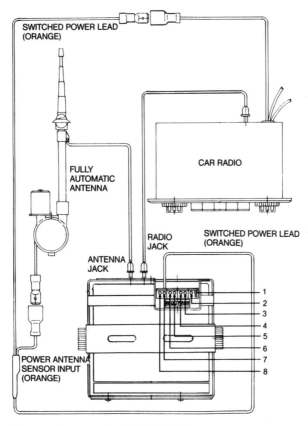

Figure 7-3: Wiring diagram for a remote paging system.

setting internal "dip switches" to either ON or OFF. *Figure 7-4* shows how these switches will look on a typical remote pager and transmitter. The dip switches are usually found near the wiring terminals on the transmitter and inside the battery compartment on the paging receiver. The dip switches should be handled with care—a ball-point pen can be a big help in setting the switches.

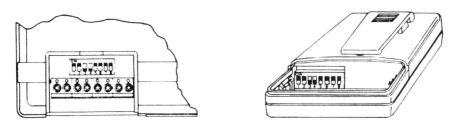

Figure 7-4: The "dip switches" on the transmitter and receiver unit.

Testing a Remote Paging System

The first step in testing a remote paging auto security system is to check all wiring connections. In particular, make sure that the connections between your car radio, antenna, and transmitter are correct. The wiring for the sensors, etc., should be checked as described in Chapter 6.

As with conventional auto security systems, the test procedure involves seeing if each sensor is capable of producing an alarm and whether the entire system performs as described in the owner's manual. (If the owner's manual gives a test procedure, follow it.) The addition of a remote paging receiver means that you will probably need someone to help you test the system. Have this person "exercise" the system by tripping all switches, motion detectors, etc., used by the system. Check the remote paging receiver to see if it produces an alarm indication (usually a combination of a "beeping" sound and a flashing LED) when someone tries to enter the vehicle with the system armed. If the pager is capable of transmitting control signals back to your car, be sure to test all of its control functions.

When performing these tests, be sure to keep the paging receiver at least three feet (one meter) from the radio antenna. If it is closer, the signal from the transmitter could "overload" the pager and cause erratic, incorrect operation of the system.

You also need to test the operating range of your system in the environments where it will be used. For example, if you plan to park the car in a garage while at work, have someone activate the alarm and see if the paging receiver can pick up the signal from your work area. If the range is inadequate or performance is erratic, try placing the pager near a window or telephone. You may have to install a separate CB antenna to get maximum range.

Don't try to increase the range of your system by internally adjusting the transmitter or adding an exteral amplifier to it. Not only is this illegal, but any extra power could damage your car radio. It may also cause improper operation of your system because the security codes may be distorted and therefore not "recognized" by the paging unit.

Other Uses for Auto Security Systems

While Chapters 6 and 7 have described how to install and use auto security systems in cars, the same systems can also be used in a variety of other vehicles such as campers, mobile homes, trailers, boats, etc. If the vehicle has a metal chassis, you can use the same components you would in a car and install them in the same manner. If the vehicle has a fiberglass or wood body (such as a boat), then you will be unable to use pin switches. However, motion detectors and micro transducers can still be used. All connections to ground (such as for a siren) should be made directly to the negative terminal of the storage battery.

Because auto security systems can be powered directly from a standard 12-volt automobile battery, they can be used in situations where it would be difficult or impractical to install a system that is powered by ac line current. Such situations include metal storage sheds, fencing, swimming pools, temporary structures, etc. The transmitter unit can be connected to a CB base station antenna to give much greater range than would be possible using a car-mounted antenna. This would be useful for covering widely scattered areas, such as buildings on a farm or at a construction site. A standard 12-volt dc power supply, such as the one shown in *Figure 7-5*, can be used to power a system in non-automotive applications.

Figure 7-5: A 12-volt dc power supply allows you to use auto alarm systems for other applications.

SUMMARY

- A remote paging auto security system includes a transmitter unit (which also serves as the control unit) mounted in the car and a pocket-sized remote paging receiver.
- Some remote pagers include a transmitter to allow you to send control signals to your auto security system. These signals can arm or disarm the system. Some remote pagers have a "panic button" to sound the system's siren.
- Never operate the transmitter in a remote paging auto security system without an antenna attached to it.
- The range of the transmitter may be increased by using a CB radio antenna.
- The remote paging unit and transmitter must use the same security code. Security codes are set using internal switches.

CHAPTER 8
CASE HISTORIES

There is no such thing as a "typical" home or auto security system. In fact, it's no exaggeration to say that each security system is unique. No two people will have the same situation or security needs, and a system that may be a good solution in one case can be totally inappropriate in another. The quality of protection you receive from your security system will depend upon the care and planning you use in designing and installing the system.

While security systems vary widely, all effective systems are planned and installed using the same fundamental procedures and logic. In this chapter, we'll examine three situations and show how the different parts of each system could be selected and installed to provide the desired protection. By following the steps outlined in these examples, your system will provide the protection you need with minimum trouble and expense.

GENERAL GUIDELINES

Before you buy or install any security system or components, there are some things you should keep in mind. While some of these may seem elementary, they can prevent major headaches for you later on:

- Check your local regulations concerning the installation and use of security systems. Obtain any necessary permits in advance.
- Review the previous chapters in this book to become knowledgeable about the various types of components available for your security system.
- Plan your installation before you start rather than trying to figure it out as you go along.
- Plan to work on only one section at a time. Break the job into basic components and steps.
- Take your time. Don't let the urge to finish quickly rush you into needless errors.

- Don't neglect non-electronic security measures, such as installing secure locks on all doors and windows.

SEPARATE COMPONENT VS. SELF-CONTAINED SYSTEMS

The first decision you must make concerning a home security system is whether to use a self-contained security system or install a system using a control unit and separate switches and sensors. Ask yourself the following questions:

- Do you rent your house or apartment?
- Are your security requirements simple?
- Do you need to protect only a single room or area?
- Is cost a major consideration?
- Are there only one or two points where an intruder could enter your home?
- Do you lack basic mechanical skills or tools?

If your answer to any of the questions above is "yes," you should give some consideration to self-contained systems. The more "yes" answers you have, the more likely that a self-contained system is best for you.

Don't overlook the versatility of permanent installations built around control units. Such systems are far more versatile and adaptable than any self-contained unit. As a general rule, you can get more comprehensive and thorough protection with separate component systems than with a self-contained system. While the initial installation and testing of separate component systems is more difficult than that for self-contained units, they can often be more convenient to use. A single key switch can activate a separate component system and provide protection for an entire house. It might take several self-contained systems to provide comparable protection, and each would have to be switched on and off individually.

When deciding on a system, remember that simplicity and reliability are virtues. A system should be no more elaborate than necessary to provide the protection you need. A system with excessive components or overly complex design may be more prone to false alarms.

A SECURITY WORKSHEET

It helps to take an inventory of your security needs before installing any system. This is most commonly done with home systems, but can also be used with auto installations. A good security inventory can point out those areas needing protection and help you decide which components and systems offer the protection you need. In fact, it's a good idea not to purchase any major home security items until you've completed a security inventory.

A security worksheet is a good technique for taking a security inventory. List each room or area in your home along with the number of doors and windows in each room. Next comes the most crucial part, identifying the types of switches or sensors you need to protect the room. Finally, note any special situations or needs you might have about that room or area. Here's a sample worksheet for the master bedroom in a typical home:

Room/Area	Doors	Windows	Sensors Needed	Other
Master bedroom	1	3	1 plunger switch 3 reed switches	Alarm device

In this example, we've identified one door and three windows as possible areas for an intruder to enter. To protect the door, a simple plunger switch installed in the door jamb can be used, while the windows can be protected by magnetic reed switches. We've also indicated a need for an alarm device of some sort in the bedroom. This process is then repeated for all other rooms in the house.

After you've completed your security worksheet, put it aside for a few days and then review it. Are there other, simpler ways to provide the protection you need in a room? In our example, a plunger switch was used to protect the door to the master bedroom. But in most cases a magnetic reed switch would work just as well and would likely be easier to install. Go through your entire security worksheet and examine the choices you've made for switches and sensors. Will they provide the protection you want? How difficult will it be to install the switches and sensors and connect them to the control unit? Would self-contained systems be a better way to protect certain areas?

When you've reviewed your security worksheet and made your final changes, you're ready to perform the actual installation of a security system.

CASE 1: INSTALLING A SYSTEM IN YOUR HOME

While a security worksheet is a big help in determining the switches and sensors you need for each room or area in your house, it doesn't help much in planning the actual wiring of your system. A plan of each floor of your house can be helpful in planning the wiring. It's best to use a separate floor diagram for each loop in your system.

In this example a control unit has three loops available: a N.C. delayed loop, a N.C. instant loop, and a N.O. instant loop. To avoid getting the N.O. instant loop confused with the N.C. instant loop, we call the N.O. instant loop the "panic" loop. We'll also assume that the control unit lets us use a siren or bell alarm, a telephone dialer, and has a pre-alarm circuit. Finally, let's assume that we want several remote status indicators so that we can tell at different points in the house whether the system is armed.

Figure 8-1 shows the connections we might make using the N.C. delayed loop. There are three main doors leading into the house: a front door, a back door, and a door leading from the garage into the dining area. Because we expect people to enter and exit using these doors, the delayed loop is used so that we will have time to disarm the system after entering. We could use magnetic reed switches, plunger switches, or a combination on the loop. Note how the last switch in the series, the one protecting the back door, is connected.

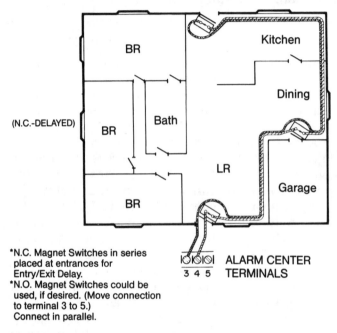

*N.C. Magnet Switches in series placed at entrances for Entry/Exit Delay.
*N.O. Magnet Switches could be used, if desired. (Move connection to terminal 3 to 5.) Connect in parallel.

ALARM CENTER TERMINALS
3 4 5

Figure 8-1: Wiring plan for a N.C. delayed loop.

Because people normally don't enter or exit a house via windows, we want to use an instant loop to protect them. *Figure 8-2* shows the connections using the N.C. instant loop to protect all the windows in the house. Magnetic reed switches are usually the easiest way to protect windows that can be opened. If we have fixed windows, such as large picture windows at the front of the house, we can also use N.C. glass breakage detectors on this loop.

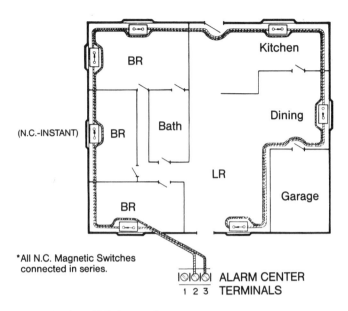

*All N.C. Magnetic Switches connected in series.

|O|O|O| ALARM CENTER
1 2 3 TERMINALS

Figure 8-2: Wiring plan for a N.C. instant loop.

At first glance, it might seem that the N.O. "panic" loop would be used for much the same purposes as the N.C. instant loop. But this is not the case. Because a "panic button" is a N.O. switch, we use this loop to activate the system when we suspect that there may be trouble (for example, if we hear a sound from the garage or yard). *Figure 8-3* shows how we can install a panic switch in each of the bedrooms, as indicated by the switches labeled (1). We can add other N.O. switches on this loop. Suppose that we have a remote key switch in the garage for arming and disarming the system. We could use a N.O. tamper switch to protect the *key switch*, as indicated by the switch labeled (2). Finally, we could add N.O. motion sensors or vibration sensors to the loop. Because this is an instant loop, the motion sensor should be located well inside the house, as indicated by (3) in *Figure 8-3*. A motion sensor placed there could provide an additional margin of protection in the event an intruder managed to get past the door and window switches. A vibration detector could be used if there is a valuable object, such as a painting, that we wish to protect in the house. Note that all the switches in *Figure 8-3* are wired in parallel because they are the N.O. type.

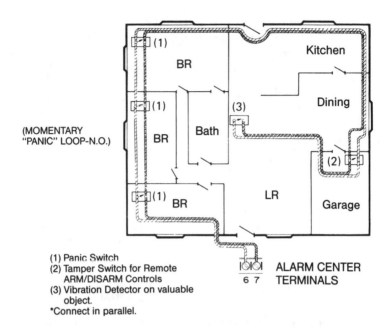

(MOMENTARY "PANIC" LOOP-N.O.)

(1) Panic Switch
(2) Tamper Switch for Remote ARM/DISARM Controls
(3) Vibration Detector on valuable object.
*Connect in parallel.

ALARM CENTER TERMINALS
6 7

Figure 8-3: Wiring plan for a N.O. instant ("panic button") loop.

We will also want to install remote key switches and system indicators wherever we might enter the house. In this example, this would mean the front, back, and garage doors. We might also want to add another key switch and indicators in the master bedroom so that we can arm the system before bedtime and check its status during the night. *Figure 8-4* shows the placement of the key switches and the wiring path of the loop. All of the key switches are connected in parallel.

The exact warning devices added to the system would depend on our particular requirements. Usually we would want a siren or bell, as indicated by (2) in *Figure 8-5*, to make a sound loud enough to alert us or neighbors in the event of an intrusion. But we might also want to add a telephone dialer, as indicated by (3). Note that the dialer is located in one of the bedrooms. This is so that it can call a programmed number and deliver its message before it could be discovered and defeated by an intruder. We also might want to use some sort of pre-alarm device near the front door to remind us to disarm the system or to let us know when a door has been opened.

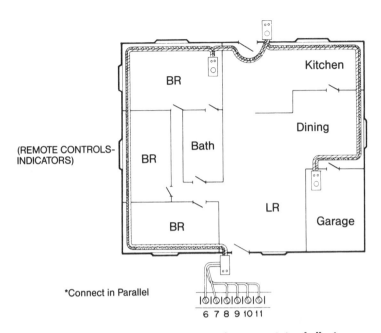

(REMOTE CONTROLS-INDICATORS)

BR

Bath

BR

BR

Kitchen

Dining

LR

Garage

*Connect in Parallel

6 7 8 9 10 11

Figure 8-4: Wiring plan for remote key switches and system status indicators.

As the various loops are planned, it's important to also plan how and where the wiring will be run. Wiring should be kept out of sight for cosmetic reasons and to prevent damage to it by pets, children, or intruders. You might find that it will be difficult or impossible to run wiring from your control unit to a certain switch or sensor. In such cases, you can try locating the switch or sensor in another area or using a self-contained security device of some sort. For example, it might be easier to install a self-contained window alarm on an isolated window than it would be to add that window to the N.C. instant loop protecting the other windows. Don't be afraid to alter or rework your floor diagrams if you encounter problems in wiring the system.

Of course, smoke alarms and sensors are an essential part of your home security system. Chapter 5 discusses the installation of these, and you'll find another floor diagram helpful in locating smoke alarms and sensors.

Before actually installing any components of your system, reread Chapters 3 and 4 for hints on installing and wiring switches and sensors. Chapter 4 also has information on testing and troubleshooting security systems.

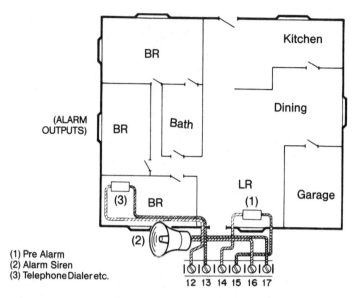

(ALARM OUTPUTS)

(1) Pre Alarm
(2) Alarm Siren
(3) Telephone Dialer etc.

12 13 14 15 16 17

Figure 8-5: Wiring plan for security system warning devices.

CASE 2: INSTALLING A SYSTEM IN YOUR CAR

A security worksheet and a planning diagram are also useful for automobile security systems. You also need to keep in mind the environments in which the car will be parked. For example, your car might normally be parked in an open parking lot during the daytime. A relatively simple alarm can provide all the protection you need in those circumstances. But you may have to park your car outdoors at night or in an unattended parking garage. In those situations, you might want to use a remote paging system, a louder siren, a motion detector, and similar measures for added protection. The right security system for your car will often depend just as much on your lifestyle and habits as it does upon the car.

Examine your car for possible security "soft spots." For example, some "hatchback" automobiles have large rear windows which serve, in effect, as the trunk lid. These make a tempting target for thieves and vandals, but conventional pin switches and motion detectors are not effective in protecting them. The solution is a shock/motion sensor such as that shown in *Figure 8-6*. This device will trigger the alarm if it is subject to shock or motion.

Figure 8-6: An electronic shock/motion detector can protect automobile "hatchbacks."

You should also carefully examine your car's doors, trunk, and hood to determine the best type of switch or sensor to protect them. Often the best protection is given by using pin switches in conjunction with a motion sensor. Pin switches are simple and reliable and offer excellent protection against entry through the doors or trunk. But pin switches offer little protection if your car is towed, jacked, or otherwise tampered with. The motion detector will protect your car against such hazards.

As an example of how one might plan an auto security system, let's assume the car to be protected is a two-door hatchback. It is a driven by a man and a woman. During the daytime, it is parked in an attended lot in plain view. If the car is parked inside an enclosed garage at night, a basic auto security system will likely provide all the protection needed. But even in this situation we might want to consider a system with a remote panic button feature. Suppose the woman frequently drives the car to a shopping mall in the evenings and usually has to park the car at some distance from the mall entrance. After shopping, she usually has to walk through a dark, poorly-lit parking lot to get to the car. A system with a remote panic button feature gives welcome reassurance in those situations. Similarly, a system with remote paging should be considered if you must park your car on the street or in an unattended lot (as in an apartment complex) at night.

Planning the wiring of an auto security system is very crucial, because the wiring is often exposed to more hazards than wiring in a home security system. Cars have sharp corners that can nick or cut wiring, and you may have to run wiring in or through places that may be difficult to access. Before deciding to install a switch or sensor in a certain location, be sure that you are able to connect it to the control unit. Because your car's chassis will be used as the ground portion of the switch circuit, make certain that each switch has a solid, electrically sound connection to the chassis. And if you're going to use your existing car door switches with your security system, know whether they are the Ford or General Motors type before beginning the installation.

It may take some experimentation to determine the best location and sensitivity setting for a motion sensor. The best spot is usually on your car's firewall. A good mechanical connection is essential, because most sensors (like pin switches) use the car chassis as the ground side of the circuit. The sensitivity control on the sensor should be adjusted in the following manner:

- Turn the alarm system on.
- Adjust the sensitivity control until the alarm sounds.
- When the alarm sounds, turn the alarm off.
- Set the sensitivity control of the motion sensor to about half the setting at which the alarm sounded.
- Turn the alarm system on again. The alarm should be silent. If not, reduce the sensitivity setting some more.
- If the alarm is silent, shake the front end of your car. The alarm should sound. If it doesn't, slightly increase the sensitivity and shake your car again. Repeat as necessary until the alarm sounds when you shake the car.

If you have installed a remote paging or panic button system, you need to test its range in situations similar to those in which it will normally be used. If the range is inadequate, or if reception of the control or paging signals is irregular, you may need to add a separate CB antenna.

The most common cause of improper or erratic operation in auto security systems is improperly installed or adjusted pin switches. Symptoms of improperly installed or functioning switches include improper entry delay operation (the alarm may sound immediately when you open a door), erratic operation of the alarm or entrance delay, and false alarms. If such symptoms are present, each pin switch should be checked for a tight fit and good electrical connection to the car chassis. Make sure each switch depresses at least 1/4" (6.35 mm) when the door, trunk, or hood is closed. Dirt can cause intermittent operation of switches. Clean the connection with a small wire brush if dirt is present on the plunger of a pin switch. You should also verify that water cannot reach the pin switches, because water can short out them out.

Another common problem area for auto security systems involves connections to ground. A ground connection can be made either to the car chassis or to the negative (black) terminal of the car battery. If a ground connection is made to the chassis, the connection must be solid electrically and mechanically. The point of the chassis where the ground connection is made should be clean and free of dirt, paint, corrosion, etc. Check each ground connection with a continuity tester or voltmeter.

CASE 3: USING AUTO SECURITY SYSTEMS IN OTHER APPLICATIONS

Auto security systems are designed to operate from 12-volt dc power supplies, and this makes them a good choice for non-automotive applications where it is difficult or impossible to use a system built around a control unit powered by 120-volt ac. Moreover, there are some functions offered by auto security systems (such as remote paging) that are not offered by conventional security systems. You might want to use an auto security system even if a reliable source of 120-volt ac is available.

There are two ways to power an auto security system in non-automotive situations. One, obviously, is to use a conventional 12-volt automobile battery. The battery should be "trickle charged" by a standard auto battery charger whenever the security system is not in use. The exact length of time a battery can power the system between charges depends upon the battery, the security system, and whether the alarm is activated while the system is in service. Normally, an auto battery can power an auto security system for several days if the alarm is not activated.

If there is a source of 120-volt ac available, you may want to power the system from a 12-volt power supply, as discussed in Chapter 7. The disadvantage of this approach is that there is no back-up power if the 120-volt ac line goes out.

Because auto security systems are designed to use the car's chassis as the ground connection point, all ground connections in other applications will have to be made to the negative terminal of the battery or 12-volt dc power supply. These connections can be made using insulated 16 to 22 gauge wire. If you're using an auto security system to protect a metal utility building or similar structure, don't try to use the building as the negative ground. An auto chassis is designed to provide a ground path for the car's electrical system. While a metal utility building might seem as if it would provide a similar ground path, this is often not the case. The walls may be electrically "isolated" from each other by nonconductive screws, paint, etc. It's best to use a separate wire connected to the negative terminal of the 12-volt dc power source.

Running a separate power and ground wire back to the power source for each switch would produce messy and likely unreliable wiring. The solution is to run a "power bus" and a "ground bus" from the system control unit and connect the various switches to the buses. All connections from the buses to the individual sensors should be soldered and then insulated using electrical tape. You'll find it useful to use different wire colors for the power and ground buses to prevent confusion.

Auto security systems are designed to use N.O. pin switches, and you can use most types of N.O. switches intended for separate component home security systems. You may have some difficulty using components intended for auto security systems, such as pin switches, in non-automotive applications. The biggest problem is that pin switches, motion sensors, and other auto security devices are designed to be grounded through the car's chassis. Connecting these to the ground bus shown in *Figure 6-13* can be tricky. The best approach is to first determine a path to electrical ground using a continuity tester or voltmeter and then solder a wire from the switch or sensor to the ground bus.

Auto security systems have some features that make them particularly well-suited for farm and rural area applications. For example, an auto security system can be used to protect fence gates or scattered buildings on a farm. If such systems are remote paging types, it would be possible to protect areas from which an audible alarm is unlikely to be heard. A CB base station antenna could be used with the control unit/transmitter for much greater range than would be possible using an auto CB antenna. Paging security systems that offer remote arm/disarm and panic button features can provide protection in special situations where conventional separate component systems would not be adequate.

Auto security systems with motion sensors can be used to protect items that could be towed away by thieves, such as trailers, boats, etc. However, don't try to use a motion sensor with an auto security system installed on a boat that will be left at a dock. There will usually be no way to adjust the sensitivity so that the motion detector offers any protection without being subject to frequenct false alarms due to the rocking of the boat.

If you do use an auto security system in another application, you must take special precautions to prevent the possibility of any part of the system, including the switches and wiring, from coming into contact with water. If the wires and switches get wet, the system will be plagued by false alarms and erratic operation. If the control unit/transmitter gets wet, it can suffer severe damage. You will also need to carefully hide the system from the view of any potential intruders.

SUMMARY

- Carefully assess your security needs to determine whether a self-contained or separate component system would be best for your situation.
- Use a security worksheet to identify those areas in your home needing protection.
- Use a floor diagram to plan the installation of each loop of a separate component security system.
- Examine your car for security "soft spots" when planning your auto security system.
- Improperly adjusted or installed pin switches are a common cause of problems in auto security systems.
- Separate power and ground buses should be used with switches when using auto security systems in non-auto applications.

LIST OF ILLUSTRATIONS

GLOSSARY OF SECURITY SYSTEM TERMINOLOGY

This glossary covers terms used in this book as well as those often found in local regulations pertaining to security systems.

Active Sensor: A sensor that creates a field and detects a disturbance in that field.

Alarm: Either a self-contained security system or an audible warning device such as a siren.

Alarm Circuit: The wiring arrangement of a security system that detects a signal from a sensor and activates a warning device.

Alarm Condition: When a security system has been activated and the warning device is operating.

Alarm Device: See Warning Device.

Alarm Output: A voltage or other signal given to another device when an alarm circuit is activated.

Alarm Reset: See Reset.

Alarm System: See Security system.

Annunciator: See Warning Device. Also used to describe an alarm monitoring device consisting of a number of visible signals, such as lamps or LEDs, indicating the status of the various loops in a security system.

Area Protection: Security of an inner space or volume of a secured area by means of a volumetric sensor.

Area Sensor: A sensor that applies to an area such as a window.

Audible Alarm Device: A sound generating device such as a siren, bell, or horn, used as part of a security system to indicate an alarm condition.

Authorized Access Switch: A switch used to make a security system, or some portion or zone of a security system, inoperative in order to permit authorized access.

Backup Battery Power: A secondary source of operating power for a security system and its associated circuitry should the AC power line fail.

Beam Interruption Alarm: See Photoelectric Sensor.

Circumvention: The defeating of a security system by the avoidance of its sensors and switches.

Closed Circuit System: A system in which the switches and sensors of each zone or loop are connected in series, usually all normally closed, so that current exists in each switch or sensor. When an activated switch or sensor breaks the circuit, or the connecting wire is cut, an alarm is transmitted for that zone.

Contact: Each one of the pair of metallic parts of a switch or relay which, by touching or separating, make or break the electrical current path.

Control Key: Key used with an authorized access switch or remote key switch.

Control Unit: A device, usually electronic, that provides the interface between the security system and the human operator and produces an alarm signal when its programmed response indicates an alarm condition. A control unit may also provide power for various sensors, sensitivity adjustments, means to select and indicate access mode, monitoring for line supervision and tamper switches, and timing of the alarm signal.

Defeat: The frustration, counteraction, or thwarting of a security system so that it fails to signal an alarm when a protected area is entered. Defeating includes circumvention.

Delayed Loop: A loop that does not indicate a violation until a specified interval after it happens.

Detection Range: The greatest distance at which a sensor will consistently detect an intruder under a standard set of conditions.

Detector: A sensor used to detect intrusion, equipment malfunctions or failure, rate of temperature rise, smoke, or fire.

End-of-Line Module: Electronic module used as the last element in a loop of smoke or thermal sensors.

Entrance Delay: The time between activating a sensor on an entrance door or gate and the sounding of a local alarm or transmission of an alarm signal upon activation of a sensor on an exit door. This delay is used if the authorized access switch is located within the protected area. It permits a person with the control key to turn on the security system and leave through a protected door or gate without causing an alarm. The delay is provided by a timer within the control unit.

False Alarm: An alarm signal transmitted in the absence of an alarm condition. These may be caused by environmental factors (such as rain, wind, temperature, or lightning), family pets, man-made electromagnetic interference, or insects. Other false alarms may be caused by operator error, inadequate grounding of the control unit, or faulty components. A certain percentage will ultimately be unknown in origin.

Foil: Thin metallic strips cemented to a protected surface (usually glass in a door or window) and connected to a closed electrical circuit. If the protected material is broken so as to break the foil as well, the circuit opens, initiating an alarm signal. Also called tape. A window, door, or other surface to which foil has been applied is said to be "taped" or "foiled".

Gap: The distance between two magnetic elements in a magnetic device, such as the space between the magnetic poles of a switch assembly.

Gel Battery: A source of direct current, usually in multiples of 2 volts (typically 6 or 12 volts total), which has the ability to provide high current over a short duration or moderate current over a long duration. A gel battery is easily recharged and maintained at a given power capacity through recharging.

Heat Sensor: See Thermal Detector.

Indicator: Usually a lamp or LED that, by becoming lit, shows that a given condition either has changed or that the status is the same. Can be either at a control unit or a remote panel.

Infrared Motion Sensor: A sensor that detects changes in the infrared light radiation from parts of a protected area. The presence of an intruder in the area changes the infrared light intensity from the direction of the intruder.

Instant Loop: A loop that indicates a violation as soon as it occurs.

Interior Protection: A line of protection along the interior boundary of a protected area including all points through which entry can be made.

Intrusion Alarm System: A security system for signaling the entry or attempted entry of a person or an object into the area protected by the system.

Ionization Smoke Alarm: Smoke alarm in which the air in a sensing chamber is ionized, permitting an electric current to flow across the sensing chamber. Smoke particles reduce the level of ionization, disrupting the electric current flow and producing an alarm.

Light-Emitting Diode (LED): A semiconductor diode that emits light. Often used as an indicator light in security systems and controls.

Line Supervision: Electronic protection of an alarm line accomplished by sending a continuous or coded signal through a circuit. A change in the circuit characteristics, such as a change in impedance due to the circuit having been tampered with, will be detected and intiate an alarm if the change exceeds a certain level. A normally closed loop is supervised.

Local Alarm: An alarm that, when activated, either makes a loud noise at or near the protected area, floods the site with light, or both.

Loop: An electrical circuit consisting of several elements (switches or sensors) connected in series.

Loop Resistance: Electrical resistance of an entire closed loop, including all connections, presented to the control unit.

Loop Response Time: The time, usually in milliseconds, that it takes for a sensor to be in a violated state before the control unit reacts.

Magnetic Switch: A switch consisting of two separate units: a magnetically actuated switch and a magnet. The switch is usually mounted in a fixed position such as a door jamb or window frame opposite the magnet. The magnet is fastened to the door or window. When the door or window is opened, the removal of the magnet allows the switch contacts to change status, either opening or closing, depending upon the design of the switch.

Master Control Panel: See Control Unit.

Mat Switch: A flat area switch that resembles a rubber mat and contains switch contact surfaces that make contact when stepped on.

Mechanical Switch: A switch in which the contacts are opened and closed by means of a depressible plunger or button. Often used with a tamper switch or a switch within the hinge assembly of a door.

Mercury Switch: A normally open switch that uses conductive mercury to close the contacts when the switch is tilted or moved.

Microwave Alarm System: An alarm system that uses microwaves as the detection method. See also Radio Frequency (RF) Motion Detector.

Monitoring Station: The central station or other area at which security guards, police, or commercial service personnel observe annunciators reporting on the condition of security systems.

Motion Sensor: A sensor that responds to the motion of anyone or anything in the protected area.

Normally Closed (N.C.) Switch: A switch, magnetic or mechanical, in which the contacts are closed (electrically conductive) when no external forces act upon the switch in its usual state.

Normally Open (N.O.) Switch: A switch in which the contacts are open or separated (electrically non-conductive) when no external forces act upon the switch in its usual state.

Open Circuit System: A system in which the switches are connected in parallel. When a switch is activated, the circuit is closed, permitting current to flow, which activates the alarm signal.

Panic Button: A circuit that, when a single button is pressed, instantly activates an alarm.

Passive Infrared Sensor: A sensor that detects natural radiation or radiation disturbances but does not itself emit the radiation on which its operation depends.

Pendulum Switch: A switch used to sense vibration or motion. The switch is designed with a set of contacts that come into contact with each other when the switch is moved or shaken.

Perimeter Protection: Protection of access to the outer limits of a protected area by means of physical barriers, sensors on physical barriers, or external sensors not associated with a physical barrier.

Photoelectric Sensor: Sometimes called an electric eye, this sensor detects a visible or invisible beam of light and responds to its complete or near complete interruption.

Photoelectric Smoke Alarm: Smoke alarm in which a beam of light is projected across a sensing area onto a photocell. Smoke particles reduce the amount of light reaching the photocell, triggering an alarm.

Piezoelectric Crystal: A crystalline material which will develop a voltage when subjected to mechanical stress or severe vibration.

Pin Switch: A small normally open plunger-type switch designed for use in autombile security systems; it uses the body of the car for the ground connection to the alarm system.

Pre-Alarm: An audible warning given by a separate sounder device indicating that a violation has occured and that, if not cleared within a specific time, the control unit will produce an alarm.

Protected Area: An area monitored by an alarm system or guards, or enclosed by a suitable barrier.

Radio Frequency (RF) Motion Detector: A sensor that detects the motion of an intruder through the use of an electromagnetic field comprised of radio waves generated over the protected area. The device operates by sensing a disturbance in the radiated RF field caused by intruder motion, typically a modulation of the field referred to as the Doppler effect. The Doppler effect is the difference in frequency of one wave to another wave that is superimposed upon it. This Doppler effect is sensed and is used to initiate an alarm signal. Most radio frequency motion detectors are certified by the Federal Communications Commission for operation as "field disturbance sensors." Units operating in the microwave frequency range are called microwave motion detectors.

Reed Switch: A type of magnetic switch consisting of electrical contacts formed by two thin, magnetically actuated metal reed-like vanes, held in a normally open position within a sealed glass envelope.

Remote Alarm: An alarm signal transmitted to a remote paging unit or monitoring station.

Reset: To restore a device to its original or normal condition after an alarm or violation signal has been transmitted.

Secure Mode: The condition of a security system in which all sensors and control units are ready to respond to any intrusion.

Security Code: A user-selectable code, usually by means of switches, that will activate a security system or remote paging receiver.

Security System: An electronic system consisting of sensors, a warning device, and a control unit designed to detect an intrusion into a protected area and to activate the warning device upon detection of an intrusion. The system may also activate a warning device if smoke or fire is detected in a protected area.

Sensor: A device designed to produce a signal or offer an indication in response to an event or stimulus within its detection zone.

Shunt: The deliberate shorting of an electrical circuit. Also refers to a key-operated switch that removes some portion of a security system from normal operation, allowing entry into a protected area without initiating an alarm signal.

Silent Alarm: A remote alarm giving no obvious local indication that an alarm has been transmitted.

Smoke Alarm: A self-contained device that reacts to visible or invisible products of combustion and produces an alarm.

Smoke Sensor: A device that reacts to visible or invisible products of combustion.

Standby Power Supply: Equipment that provides a source of power to a system in the event that the primary source of power is interrupted or lost. Generally, it consists of batteries and charging circuits.

Supervised Lines: Interconnecting lines in a security system that are electrically checked to detect tampering. See Line Supervision.

Supervisory Circuit: An electrical path, wired or wireless, that sends information on the status of a sensor to a control unit or annunciator.

Tamper Switch: A switch installed in such a way as to be activated by an attempt to remove the enclosure of a security system or one of its components.

Telephone Dialer: A device that, when activated, automatically dials one or more pre-programmed telephone numbers, such as those of the police or fire departments, and plays a pre-recorded voice or coded message giving the nature and location of the alarm.

Thermal Detector: A device that reacts if the temperature in the protected area rises above a certain point.

Transducer: A device that produces an electric current in response to vibration, motion, or shock.

Trouble: An electrical state, such as a short circuit, within a loop that prevents normal arming and subsequent operation.

Ultrasonic: A sound wave whose frequency lies above the typical upper limit of human hearing, which is 20,000 cycles per second or 20 kHz. This sound wave frequency is used in ultrasonic motion detectors.

Violation: When a loop, circuit, or switch has been tampered with and its state has been affected to result in an alarm being initiated.

Volumetric Sensor: A sensor with a detection zone that extends over a volume, an area in three dimensions, such as an entire room, part of a room, or a hallway. Ultrasonic motion and microwave detectors are an example of this type of sensor.

Warning Device: Any siren, bell, light, telephone dialer, or other device to indicate when a violation has taken place in a security system.

Zone: A geographical section of the premises under security. Often used synonymously with loop.

Zoned Circuit: An electrical path that provides continual protection for parts or zones of the protected area while releasing normally used doors and windows for access.

INDEX

Alarm devices:
bells, 4-2
connecting to control units, 4-2
outdoor mounting of, 4-5
sirens, 4-1
strobe lights, 4-4
telephone dialers, 4-2 to 4-4

Automatic timer systems, 1-10 to 1-12

Automotive security systems:
basic components of, 6-1, 6-2
control units for, 6-7
installation example, 8-8 to 8-11
installation of, 6-8 to 6-13
motion detectors for, 6-5
pin switches for, 6-4
placement of switches and sensors, 6-8, 6-9
remote paging systems, 7-1 to 7-3
sirens for, 6-6
testing of, 6-14, 6-15
using door frame switches in, 6-11
wiring for, 6-12, 6-13
using in non-automotive applications, 8-11 to 8-13

Control units:
backup batteries for, 2-14
grounding of, 2-10
installation of, 2-8 to 2-10
internal circuitry, 2-1, 2-2
powering of, 2-10
remote key switch for, 2-8
testing of, 2-12, 2-13